ENERGY:
The New Frontier
in Reflexology

By
Christine Issel

ENERGY: The New Frontier in Reflexology
©2020 by Christine Issel

New Frontier Publishing
www.christine issel.com
christinec.issel@gmail.com
ISBN 978-0-9625448-4-2

Printed in the United States of America

The information in this book is not intended as a substitute for medical care. If you have a health problem, consult a medical professional.

DEDICATION

This book is dedicated to those reflexologists around the globe who are brave enough to entertain new concepts that can move our profession forward.

ACKNOWLEDGMENTS

I appreciate and am grateful to the technical assistance provided by Alonzo Bartley and Ariana Thaxter for their graphics; Cheryl Burke for her headshot; April Dulong for her work; Adrianne Fahey for proofing—since I can never leave anything alone any mistakes are my own, not hers. I am thankful to Kristi Gabriel for her ear and advice; Christopher Stola, for his friendship and computer scanning; and Patricia Thaxter for her patience, InDesign layout help and belief in reflexology. My thanks also to Louise for her encouragement and support of this endeavor and others. Without the assistance from them this book would have remained a lecture.

Furthermore, my thanks to the authors of quantum medicine for their forward thinking that has spurred along my thoughts and expanded my horizons for over 25 years.

TABLE OF CONTENTS

Beginning Our Journey Into Energy

The metamorphosis of a caterpillar into a butterfly is one of the most remarkable things in nature. The insect apparently digests itself, using enzymes triggered by hormones. Then, from the pupa, a whole new animal develops—one with wings!

Time and growth produce changes in institutions, too. Sometimes, they go through a metamorphosis and change into something very different. The focus of this book is "energy," with the question to be answered: Can the concept be explained in terms acceptable from a scientific, intellectual and critical thinking point of view while at the same time satisfy those using it in the context of a therapeutic approach?

Historically there has always been a great deal of skepticism and resistance towards giant leaps in established paradigms. The subject of subtle or finer energies outside our sensory systems is no exception.

Until the last few decades, their existence was difficult to prove because they couldn't be weighed and measured. However, with the advent of quantum physics and mechanics, a new turning point exists that takes science and medicine in new directions and opens the door for the emergence of holistic healing therapies such as reflexology. Researchers are finding that the human body responds to the environment through ambient fields like color, sound, light, electricity and magnetism.

Many authors over the years have written about reflexology, energy and the techniques they employ. Specific techniques on how to physically work with unseen energies is beyond the scope of this work in that the purpose of this effort is to expand your theoretical knowledge base, not instruct the reader in basic or advanced techniques.

Though the focus of this book is on reflexology, the information contained herein easily applies to all forms of manual or energetic disciplines, methods and spiritual persuasions. There is so much more to what we do than what we are used to seeing and doing; what we've accepted as the ways things have been for years.

I do not claim that the information presented is original. The information comes from many sources. By sharing some new concepts, it is hoped ideas will be triggered and result in further study, and more research with energy will come about for the benefit of the practitioner and the client alike.

The goal of this book is to take us on a journey that expands our thoughts and awareness of various energies that surround us and with which we work when performing our work whether we acknowledge this connection or not.

Wishing you a successful journey wherever your life takes you.

Chapter 1: ENERGY

It is said the difference between a dead man and a live one is more than a pulse. Most important, the dead lack the ability to turn matter into energy or energy into matter. Life cannot exist without energy for energy is the basis of all life and a vital factor in healing.

Reflexology is not simply the pushing of points on the feet, hands or outer ears to affect the body. It is much more than that. The goal of this book is to expand our thoughts and awareness of various energies that surround us.

In physics, energy is defined simply as the capacity to do work, and energy exchanges are observable and measurable. Energy therapists, in contrast, use the term to loosely describe a kind of universal life force that influences health or the capacity of acting or producing an effect.

I am aware of the looseness with which the term "energy" tends to be used in alternative or complementary healing circles. I attribute this mostly to our lack of scientific exploration and understanding of energy in all of its forms. Energy when applied to healing is thought to be too mysterious to be approached by the serious-minded. It is true that only a small fraction of it has been scientifically observed, described and or quantified. While we lack this kind of scientific, in-depth understanding of *all* forms of energy, approximate terms and definitions will need to be used in the interim to roughly describe phenomena that still awaits proper exploration.

Since the sixteen hundreds and the work of Descartes (1598-1650) and Newton (1642-1727) until recently, traditional science, classical anatomy, and western medicine have considered that the human body operates largely through the following sequence: Function (physiology), structure (anatomy) and chemistry (hormones).

When the body is not functioning properly, the cause has been attributed to structural defects in the system arising out of chemical imbalance; hence, the focus on drugs and surgery to correct the imbalance. Notice this does not take into consideration the mind-emotions or the healthy functioning of the body.

Why Study Energy?

As Dolores Krieger, developer of Therapeutic Touch, says so beautifully, "Love itself, I found, is not enough to be truly therapeutic; you have to understand what you are doing. You have to act knowledgeably."

Studying energy and its effect within the body is important because it gives:

- Reflexology breadth and depth—its legitimacy and credibility;
- Standards of excellence in education and training that are the foundation upon which a profession is built and the safety of the public is assured;
- The opportunity for the field to advance and possibly provides a new definition for our work;
- The practitioner greater confidence, understanding,

and appreciation of anatomy—both conventional and energetic;

- An understanding of the interconnectedness of everything in the universe, bringing forth in the individual respect for all things;
- The reflexologist the opportunity to grow within themselves on all levels; and
- The client the best environment for healing.

In my view, reflexology is a blend of physical and energy-based medicines. The conventional medicine is the bio-medical model and based on what can be seen, weighed and measured while the foundation of the energy-based model is on the unseen forces at work. Reflexology has a connection to science, energy and integrative medicine therapies.

A common denominator in many techniques and disciplines of energy medicine is the therapist and their clients describing the feeling of energy moving during a session. In essence, this is the vital energy or life force of the body circulating to create balance between the cells, tissues and organs and assists the body to balance internally so that it can function optimally to the best of its ability.

With reflexology, beyond the physical body, it is energy we work with whether consciously or unconsciously, and the effects of reflexology go beyond the seen to the unseen. This multifaceted effect is why reflexology, in my experience, is the most dynamic 'healing' therapy there is. Any time we perform reflexology, it goes about its work to bring as much balance as possible to any imbalance found in the body regardless of where we work on the feet, hands or outer ears. If energy is blocked, the tissue relating to the blockage becomes dis-eased. Reflexology affects imbalances on the physical as well as on the energy bodies.

In this endeavor, we will be speaking about two kinds of energy: both energy commonly accepted by science and subtle energy of esoteric wisdom and their effects on health. Energy is the new frontier—it bridges the gap between science and the subtle energy of the body.

Just as reflexology made a transition from zone therapy of Dr. William FitzGerald through Dr. Joe Shelby Riley to Eunice Ingham and into the charts and tradition of reflexology we have today, this book takes us beyond classical reflexology based on Newtonian science to quantum physics, subtle energies and consciousness. An in-depth discussion on the nature of complementary therapies is beyond the scope of this report; however, no integrative therapies, or their combination with reflexology, are right or wrong. Do not be limited but continue to expand your knowledge base by studying and taking specialty classes. Attending conferences is also an excellent way to be introduced to international speakers who bring with them new ideas and hands-on work.

There are three cautions as you read through this book:

1. It is said that advances are made in answering questions, and discoveries are made by questioning answers. Don't believe anything I or anyone else has written or said. I do not make the claim that everything presented is unequivocally accurate and should be accepted without question. Believe your experience, your critical thinking, and check with your intuition using applied kinesiology (more on how to do this later).

2. With any course, take that which you resonate with and leave the rest. Integrate what you have learned into your practice or thought process and make the information "yours"—ultimately it will, in all likelihood, not be exactly as you've been taught.

3. Keep your ego in check. Do not rush to judgments of a client based on taking only a weekend or short course. For

example, any condition reported by the client or that you find may have a complex or unknown origin that may not be uncovered in the initial interview. Therefore it is wise to pay attention to what your hands are telling you, not only what you discover or what the client shares with you. This discernment comes with education and practice. As a practitioner, it is not about you and what you want as it is about your client.

Chapter 2: THE SCIENCE OF ENERGY

"In essence, what appears solid is actually a flowing mass of subatomic particles frozen into what appears as solid mass and connected to all other things through an energetic field or matrix."
— Albert Einstein (1879-1955)

Energy

That energy exists and its behavior has been well known for centuries and is part of classical physics. By 1884, it was estimated 10,000 physicians in the USA were using electricity for therapeutic purposes without the blessing of science. The Flexner Report of 1909 established science as the basis for medicine and altered medicine to a reliance on drugs and surgery. This was a shift in the fundamental argument over the philosophy and nature of life—that is, mechanism vs. vitalism. The Flexner Report won the day and overhauled medical education, resulting with the use of electricity to heal being abolished and ultimately excluded legally from clinical practice as being quackery.

Dr. William Tiller, Ph.D. professor emeritus of Stanford University, illustrates the accepted scientific process through which conventional medicine works in this way:

Function ———> Structure ———> Chemistry
(physiology) <—(anatomy) <———(hormones)

When the body is not functioning properly, the cause is seen arising from structural defects in the body caused by chemical imbalances or imbalances in the function of a system, organs and/or tissue. This process flows in both directions, from chemistry to structure impeding function and vice versa so in a way the question is: Which comes first, the chicken or the egg?

As Richard Gerber, M.D. states in *Vibrational Medicine*, "Research in the last several decades has shown that biological fields are not just by-products or physiological processes, they are part of the mechanism by which the body communicates with itself and today there is more sophisticated science to support electromagnetic medicine."

Quantum Mechanics

Quantum mechanics is the science dealing with the behavior of matter and light on the atomic and subatomic levels. Matter and energy are in some ways different forms of the same thing. Matter is anything that has mass and takes up space or volume. All matter is made up of atoms. Nature stores energy everywhere: in atoms, in molecules, in every particle of matter. Matter and energy are primarily electrical in nature. Matter is composed of particles of electrons and protons, which are electrically charged.

An atom is the smallest unit into which matter can be divided without the release of electrically charged particles. Most of the atom is empty space. The rest consists of a positively charged nucleus of protons and neutrons surrounded by a cloud of negatively charged electrons. Electrons have mass and so are considered matter and not pure energy. Energy can neither be created nor destroyed, but it can be changed from one form to another. When that change happens, some of the energy is usually released.

Protons, Electrons, Neutrons

A closer look indicates a proton is one of the components found in the nucleus of every atom. Along with neutrons, protons make up the nucleus, held together by a strong force. It has a positive electric charge. Protons are nearly the same size as neutrons and are much larger than electrons. The same number of protons and electrons exactly cancel one another and form a neutral atom, a neutron.

An electron has a charge of negative electricity. They are the primary carrier of electricity in solids and can be either free traveling around the nucleus of an atom or bound to the nucleus of an atom. Like all charged particles, negative charges create electric fields around them. Atoms join to create complex molecules from the cells to organs of our body, creating quantum fields as they become intricate and intensified.

In spite of quantum mechanics, energy still remains a mystery. It is agreed that the sum of energy in the universe is constant (a closed circuit) but constantly changing. The conservation of energy principle states that energy can neither be destroyed nor created. Instead, energy just transforms from one form into another.

Types of Energy

There are many kinds of energy—*some say 20 types of energy.* Scientists have learned to produce electricity in many ways— through the use of motion, light, heat, and pressure. This is what happens when coal is burned, for instance. To bring energy transformation down to everyday life, examples include a television changing electrical energy into sound and light energy. A toaster changes electrical energy into thermal energy and light. A car changes chemical energy from fuel into thermal energy and mechanical energy. Plants convert light energy to chemical energy through photosynthesis. Friction converts kinetic energy to thermal energy. Ocean waves convert mechanical energy to electrical energy. Geothermal energy in geologically active regions of the world can be harnessed as electrical energy.

The process of fission (splitting atoms) and fusion (combining atoms) gives us nuclear energy. Another name for stored energy is potential energy. As water falls over a waterfall, its gravitational potential energy is first transformed into kinetic energy, then into thermal energy when it hits the ground. During bungee jumps, gravitational potential energy is converted to elastic potential energy. Whenever anything that has an electric charge comes in contact with the earth, the charge is carried off. This is called grounding an electric charge or current. This does not mean the charge disappears. It simply changes direction.

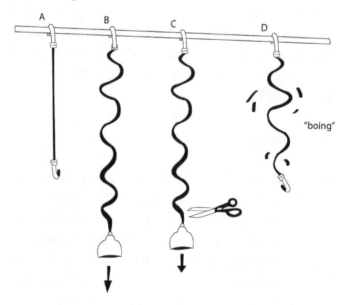

"boing"

Energy changing from one form to another:

A - Bungee cord suspended from the ceiling indicating potential and gravitational energy.
B - Weight is added to convert the potential energy of the elastic cord to mechanic and kinetic energy of motion.
C - The weight is cut so kinetic energy of motion is released..
D- The cord snaps back to its original position and now creates a sound energy.

Energies in the Body

In reference to the human body, any kind of motion taking place in the body requires mechanical energy. In the digestive process, chemical energy from food is converted to mechanical energy when the food is broken down and absorbed in the muscles. The chemical energy from food can also be converted to thermal energy to keep the body warm. And the energy of motion (kinetic energy) and the energy associated with position (potential energy) in a raised hand or elastic energy in tendons and fascia are collectively called mechanical energy. For any kind of muscle movement to occur in the body, stored potential energy is converted to chemical energy that is changed to mechanical energy as contraction of muscle (kinetic energy) occurs. In the nervous system, energy is exchanged in the form of electricity. All action produces electrical energy fields.

Electricity

Electricity is the mysterious something out of which everything in the universe is made. We can see the result of the presence of electricity but no one knows what electricity is. Simply stated, electricity is a form of energy. In defining electricity *Tabor's Cyclopedic Medical Dictionary* states, "Electricity is a form of energy that is generated by the interactions of positive and negative charges that exhibits magnetic, chemical, mechanical, and thermal effects."

If electrons are piled up at one end of a conductor and the other end has fewer electrons, the excess electrons will tend to flow toward the point where there are fewer electrons. Thus the electron current will flow through the conductor from the negative end to the positive end. It is not simply the potential energy at the two ends of the conductor that causes an electric current to flow. The force or "pressure" that moves the electrons from one point to another is known as the potential difference or the electromotive (electron-moving) force.

An important fact is that an electric current resembles a circle. That is why it is called a circuit, which means it is continuous, without beginning and without an end. Electricity can flow only in a complete circuit. If the circuit is broken, electricity cannot flow. When you turn on an electric current, you are not making electricity; you are merely allowing it to flow. The current source already exists. For example, when you turn on an electric light switch, the electric circuit is completed and the current begins to flow. You break the circuit and stop the flow of electricity when the circuit is incomplete or switched "off."

Electricity and Magnetism

Electricity and magnetism are similar but different. Electricity creates magnetism, and magnetism can produce electricity. When any force is exerted over an area, all the space into which the force reaches is called its field. This field can extend out in all directions. An electric current is always surrounded by a magnetic field. The field exists only as long as the current flows. As soon as the current stops, the magnetic field disappears. Peter Lund Frandsen of Denmark, when addressing attendees at the 2001 ICR Conference in Rome, stated, "Whenever there is an electric current, a flow of electrons, this always sets up a magnetic field in the surroundings."

Electro-Magnetic Current

Our earth itself is a giant magnet with positive and negative poles. As indicated, the body produces its own magnetic fields. Iron is known to be especially susceptible to magnetization, and the human blood carries relatively large amounts of iron, thus the body is seen to generate a magnetic field of its own. Potassium and sodium also contribute charged particles to the body's overall electric-magnetic fields.

Dr. Robert Becker, a respected orthopedic surgeon and author of *The Body Electric* and *Cross Currents*, suggests there is proof the body is an electrical unit operating within an electrical web and an electrical energetic field surrounding the body. Becker found that the points along the acupuncture meridians enhance the electromagnetic current flowing in the body. It was detected that the meridians had the electrical characteristics of transmission lines, while skin not associated with meridians did not.

Electricity and Healing

Generally the electrical and magnetic fields generated by tissues and organs that have important biological purposes have been ignored by medical science. When acknowledging that energy fields exist, these fields have been widely thought to be mere by-products of cellular activities, useful for diagnosis only. Despite this bias, through biology, bio-medical science has advanced with the study of the electrical properties of living systems, and various useful diagnostic tools have developed that involve recording the electrical fields produced by organs such as the heart (the electrocardiogram), the other muscles (electromyography), the eyes (electroretinogram), and the brain (electroencephalogram), Magnetic Resonance Imaging (MRI) and functional Magnetic Resonance Imaging (fMRI) and others.

With the introduction of quantum physics, electricity in the form of energy, and biology, the bio-medical model emerged. Dr. Tiller created an equation to explain this model.

Function ——> Structure ——> Chemistry ——> Electromagnetic fields
(physiology) <–(anatomy) <——(hormones) <——(energy)

Still, this process flows in both directions. The law of physics states that energy cannot be destroyed, merely changed; hence, all energy in the body is in a constant state of flux, circulating between all tissue and systems.

In turn, our definition of reflexology could be expanded to indicate: Reflexology is a discipline within the integrative medicine field that maps out the reflection of the entire body predominantly on the feet, hands and outer ears. It involves the communication of the body through its neural pathways (nervous system), chemically (through the hormones, endocrine and circulatory systems), mechanically (through the fascia system) and the electromagnetic fields, facilitating deep relaxation and assisting the body to function optimally.

Chapter 3: ELECTROMAGNETICS OF THE BODY

O ver the ensuing century since Flexner's Report, progress has taken place in the study of electrical properties of living systems in electrobiology, and tools have been developed that have recorded the electrical fields produced by organs.

Dual Nervous System

Traditionally, the nervous system is viewed as the fundamental energy system in the body. Its operation is studied by measuring electrical fields generated during the transmission of nerve impulses. As electric currents always give rise to magnetic fields, the nervous system is also a source of some of the biomagnetic fields present within and around the body (also known as the aura). Moreover, the nervous system regulates all muscular movements and is, therefore, key to converting thoughts into energetic actions. This is defined in physics as stated that the kinetic energy of movement changed to gravitational potential energy as an object (the limb) is lifted.

The nervous system is composed of neurons conducting information from place to place as electrical impulses. This is a bi-functioning system. The classical nervous system is composed of neurons and the system of the connective tissue. Some signals are digital and others analog in nature. The digital system provides high-speed, high-volume information transfer. It is a global system, integrating and regulating processes through the body. This system is responsible for sensation and movement. The analog system, composed of perineural cells, conducts information from place to place at relatively slow, varying, direct currents. These slow waves communicate "point to point" and are ideally suited for precise control of individual functions such as wound healing and injury repair. While functions differ, the concept of the two-fold nature of the nervous system is a similar model for the other major systems in the body.

Circulatory System

One of the primary channels for the flow of electrical energy through the body is the circulatory system. Each heartbeat begins with a pulse of electricity through the heart muscle. This electricity arises because a large number of charged particles (ions of iron, sodium, potassium, chloride, calcium, and magnesium) flow across the muscle membranes to excite contraction. These currents also spread into the surrounding tissues. Some of the flow of electricity from the heart is through the circulatory system, which is an excellent conductor of electricity because of its high iron and salt content. As the circulation carries blood to every tissue, heart electricity flows everywhere in the body which the electrocardiogram can pick up from anywhere on the skin. It is a basic law in physics that when an electric current flows through a conductor, a magnetic field is created in the surrounding space. It is from electric currents that magnetic fields arise. The heart produces a strong, pulsating magnetic field spreading out in front of and behind the body and extends indefinitely into space.

Heart pulses, measured in the order of their velocities, are the electromagnetic pulse (measured by the electrocardiogram and the magnetocardiogram), followed by a sound pulse, a pressure pulse and then a temperature pulse. New electrophysiological studies correlate emotions with heart rates. For instance, when frustration is experienced, the heartbeat is irregular, and when appreciation is experienced, the heartbeat is more consistent or calm.

Besides the heart, contractions of other muscles produce their own electrical fields that are recorded by electromyography. Every muscle in the body produces magnetic pulses when it contracts. The larger muscles produce larger fields, and the smaller muscles, such as those that move and focus the eye, produce very tiny fields. In comparison to the heart fields, the fields of the brain are weak. The brain field, like the heart field, is not confined to the organ that produces it. We refer to "brain waves" as though they are confined to the brain, but they are not. The fields of all of the organs spread throughout the body and into the space around it.

The Electromagnetic Spectrum

The broad range of visible light wavelengths is known as the electromagnetic spectrum and electromagnetic radiation (EM). Electromagnetic radiation is a stream of mass-less proton particles, each traveling in a wave-like pattern at the speed of light. Electromagnetic radiation is transmitted in waves or particles at different wavelengths and frequencies.

Two of the most utilized frequencies are gamma rays and radio waves. Gamma-rays are penetrating electromagnetic radiation arising from the radioactive decay of atomic nuclei. They create charged radicals in any material they travel through. In the human body, it causes mutations in DNA and damages cellular mechanisms. In large doses, it is enough to kill cells and cause radiation poisoning. Gamma-rays can be used to treat cancer.

Radio waves are electromagnetic waves, not sound waves. A radio wave is created when an electric field and magnetic field join. The radio wavelength on the electromagnetic spectrum is longer than infrared light and has a lower frequency than microwaves. Radio waves have frequencies as high as 300 gigahertz to as low as 30 hertz. Large doses of radio waves are believed to cause cancer, leukemia and other disorders. Some people claim that the very low frequency electromagnetic fields (EMF) from overhead power cables near their homes and from cell phones affect their health.

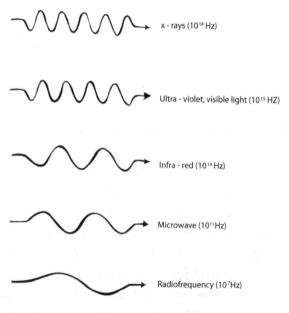

x - rays (10^{18} Hz)

Ultra - violet, visible light (10^{15} HZ)

Infra - red (10^{14} Hz)

Microwave (10^{11} Hz)

Radiofrequency (10^{7} Hz)

Different energy waves based on their Hertz frequency.

Radio waves are used for communications and radar. The prime purpose of radio is to convey information from one place to another through the intervening media (i.e., air, space, nonconducting materials) without wires. Besides being used for transmitting sound and television signals, radio is used for the transmission of data in coded form, navigation and air-traffic control, cellular telephones and even remote-controlled toys.

Biophotonics - The Power of Light

Photonics is the science and technology of generation, manipulation and detection of light—it uses photons, quantum-like particles of light, instead of electrons to transmit, process, and store information. Photonics is related to electronics and photons. Biophotonics denotes a combination of biology and photonics. The invention of lasers, a concentrated source of monochromatic and highly directional light, revolutionized photonics in the 1960s and brought us technological advancements such as bar-code scanners, CD players, and, fluorescence microscopes.

Today, biophotonics is widely regarded as the key science upon which the next generation of clinical tools and biomedical research instrumentation will be based. Although nature has used the principle of biophotonics to harness light for photosynthesis and to create vision for millennia, it wasn't until about 20 years ago that a substantial transfer of photonics technologies to biological applications began to transform medical and life sciences.

Now, thanks to brighter, light-emitting dyes, faster and more sensitive detectors, automation technology, and computing capacity that can handle storing vast amounts of image data, it is possible for scientists to probe the molecular mechanisms of life at unprecedented resolutions. The convergence of technological advances offers opportunities to understand the physiology of human disease and to find new ways to treat it.

Biophotons are emitted from the cells of our body and from our DNA, sparking an elevation of consciousness when triggered. Increasingly, science agrees we are more than the atoms and molecules that make up our bodies but beings of light as well. Biophotons can be released through mental intention and may regulate processes within cell-to-cell communication and DNA.

Biophotons are known as ultra-weak photon emissions with a visibility 1,000 times lower than the sensitivity of our naked eye. While not visible to us, these particles of light (or waves, depending on how you are measuring them) are part of the visible electromagnetic spectrum and are detectable via sophisticated, modern instrumentation. They are believed to be produced as a result of energy metabolism within our cells, or as a by-product of biochemical reactions in which excited molecules are produced from bio-energetic processes. Apparently, biophotons are used by our cells and DNA to communicate and store information that facilitates energy information transfer that is several orders of magnitude faster than chemical transmission. Research suggests that light stimulation can generate biophotons that conduct along the neural fibers, probably as neural communication signals.

Even human intention itself may have a basis in biophotons. Intention is defined as a directed thought to perform a determined action. Thoughts can affect inanimate objects and practically all living things from single-cell organisms to human beings. The emission of light particles (biophotons) seems to be the mechanism through which an intention produces its effects. All living organisms emit a constant current of photons as a means to direct instantaneous, non-local signals from one part of the body to another and to the outside world. Biophotons are stored in the intracellular DNA. Direct intention manifests itself as electric and magnetic energy. They seem to operate as highly coherent frequencies capable of changing the molecular structure of matter.

Medical Biophotonics

Medical biophotonics is leading to a wide range of new diagnostic methods and therapeutic applications. Current examples include Coherence Optical Tomography (OCT), which has revolutionized the field of ophthalmology by allowing the early diagnosis of macular degeneration in the retina, and Photodynamic Therapy approaches for treatment of cancers by retarding the growth of new blood vessels and vasculature. The recognition of biophotons moves science toward the area of invisible, vibrational energy medicine.

The Body's Circadian Biophoton Output

Because the metabolism of the body changes in a circadian fashion, biophoton emissions also vary during daytime. Research has mapped out distinct anatomical locations within the body where biophoton emissions are stronger and weaker, depending on the time of the day. Generally, the fluctuation in photon counts over the body was lower in the morning than in the afternoon. The thorax-abdomen region emitted the lowest and most constant counts. The upper extremities and the head region emitted the most and increased over the day.

The Body's Biophoton Outputs Are Governed by Solar and Lunar Forces

Research has found meditation and herbs affect biophoton output. It appears that modern science is only now coming to recognize that the human body can receive and emit energy and information directly from the light given off from the sun. The role of melanin, the brown skin pigment, is capable of transforming ultraviolet light energy into heat in a process known as "ultra-fast internal conversion;" more than 99.9% of the absorbed UV radiation is transformed from potentially DNA-damaging, ultraviolet light into harmless heat. There is also a growing realization that the sun and moon affect biophoton emissions through gravitational influences.

DNA Is Programmed By Words and Frequencies

The human genome is packed with at least four million gene switches that reside in bits of DNA that once were dismissed as "junk," but it turns out that so-called junk DNA play critical roles in controlling how cells, organs and other tissues behave. This discovery is considered a major medical and scientific breakthrough that has enormous implications for human health and consciousness, because many complex diseases appear to be caused by tiny changes in hundreds of gene switches.

As scientists delved into the "junk"—parts of the DNA that are not actual genes containing instructions for proteins—they discovered a complex system that controls genes. At least 80 percent of this DNA is active and needed. Another 15-17 percent has higher functions scientists are still decoding.

According to the finding of Russian researchers, our DNA is not only responsible for the construction of our body but also serves as data storage and in communication. Russian linguists found that the genetic code, especially in the apparently junk DNA, follows the same rules as our human languages. The rules of syntax (the way in which words are put together to form phrases and sentences), semantics (the study of meaning in language forms) and the basic rules of grammar were compared. It was found that the alkalines of our DNA follow regular grammar and do have set rules just like our languages. This scientifically explains why affirmations, autogenous training, hypnosis and the like can have such strong effects on humans and their bodies. It is entirely normal and natural for our DNA to react to language.

Visible Light and Color as Energy

Think of light like a musical chord made up of seven notes. If you were to play one of the notes individually, you'd hear one sound. The notes making up a chord sound beautiful because each of the notes has a different sound. Likewise, light is made up of vibrating energy, and the spectrum of color is light vibrating at different speeds. As you look at one part of the spectrum of light, you see one color, and all of the energies put together create the color spectrum as we see in a rainbow or when a stream of white light is bent through a prism.

Newton chose to divide the visible spectrum into seven colors out of a belief derived from the ancient Greek sophists, who thought there was a connection between the colors, the musical notes, the known objects in the solar system, and the days of the week. The colors of the rainbow, ROYGBIV, each with their own frequency, are: Red, Orange, Yellow, Green, Blue, Indigo, and Violet. Red is at the top edge of the rainbow, and violet is at the bottom edge, with the other colors in between. In the visible light spectrum the color red has the longest wavelength followed by orange, yellow, green, blue, indigo and finally violet with the shortest wavelength.

Sound, Color and Brain Waves

All our senses, physical and those beyond the physical, function in part by receiving and responding to some form of energy. Physical vision depends on the energy of light waves striking the eye. Physical hearing senses the vibrational energy of sound waves. Taste and smell function through chemical energy reactions between certain molecules and the receptor cells of the tongue and olfactory areas.

It is known that sound and light are forms of radiant energies that have different wavelengths. Sound, color, the fragrances of essential oils, emotions and gemstones have all been found to emit unique vibrational frequencies or energies at different vibratory rates producing different notes in music and colors of the rainbow.

The process of seeing and recognizing a color occurs within ourselves and is projected outwards. We see or recognize color when photons of light enter the retina where they are transformed into electrical impulses. These impulses reach the brain through electrochemical reactions in the nerve cells. The brain then transfers these reactions into the picture that we see projected outside of our bodies.

Only a small portion of light on the color spectrum is available to the human eye. Our brain interprets color based on the wavelength of light transmitted from your retina to your brain. As light passes through your eye, it hits color cells called cones. Your eye has three color cones that enable you to see a variety of color based on how the wavelengths are mixed. Your cones can see green, blue and red. When a light hits an object, some of the light is absorbed and some bounces back off the object. If that object is a red apple, for example, most of the light wavelengths, except red, are absorbed, and the red light bounces off, and your eye then sees the apple as red.

You have between six and seven million cones, or photoreceptors, in your retinas that are concentrated into a small area, approximately 0.3 mm wide. With three different color cones, humans see color better than most mammals. However, there are other life forms that see more of the light spectrum, such as some insects that may see ultraviolet light that is invisible to humans, or birds that have four types of cones, enabling them to see shorter wavelengths than humans.

The visible light spectrum is part of the electromagnetic spectrum, and its wavelengths range approximately from 380nm for violet to 740nm for red.

- Color is a wave travelling through space. Depending on the wavelength—the space between the peaks measured in nanometers (nm)—our eyes register different colors.

- Sine Wave is the measurement of energy used to depict frequency, vibration, and waves. It is a waveform, a single frequency, repeated indefinitely in time.

Just as some sound waves of a higher or lower vibration are not heard by the human ear, the same can be said of colors. In this case, we can liken these vibratory rates to an airplane propeller. When the propeller is stationary, the individual blades are easily seen. As the propeller turns, it becomes more difficult to see them as separate blades, and as the speed increases, they soon become invisible to the eye, yet their effects can be sensed through the disturbance of the air and the noise, or sound, created.

There are many sound frequencies that are considered to be very beneficial for the human body. They help harmonize the body and mind as one, thereby making it stronger as it achieves wholeness.

The Hertz (Hz) is the unit of frequency in the International System of Units and is defined as one cycle per second. It is named for German physicist, Heinrich Rudolf Hertz (1857-1894). Hertz was the first person to provide conclusive proof of the existence of electromagnetic waves. Below are some of the best-known frequencies that can be linked to their effect on the human body:

- 285 Hz – This is a healing signal for cells and tissues to rejuvenate.
- 396 Hz – This frequency frees the listener from fear and guilt, thereby making room for positive emotions with a higher vibration.
- 528 Hz – This frequency reputedly repairs damaged DNA and cells. It also awakens the consciousness of a person.
- 639 Hz – The vibration linked with the heart, it encourages feelings of love for both yourself and your significant other. It is helpful to balance relationships.
- 741 Hz – For those who are constantly exposed to electromagnetic radiation, this frequency detoxifies the cells and heals them. It is also able to empower a person, giving them the drive they need to realize their desires.
- 852 Hz – Similar to 639 Hz, it activates the intuition of a person.
- 963 Hz – Not only does this stimulate the pineal gland, it also returns the body to its original state of perfection.

Dr. Paul Nogier (1908-1996), through his research with the subtle energies of the body, identified seven frequencies and their effect a little differently; specific body tissues were in resonance with specific frequencies according to their embryologic origin.

Musical Frequency	Hz	Activity
A	292	Cellular Vitality – Resonates with the outermost tissue of the body (the ectoderm) that forms the skin, glands, nerves, eyes, ears, teeth, brain and spinal cord.
B	584	Nutritional Metabolism - Resonates with the innermost tissue (the endoderm) that forms the lining of the intestinal tract, the lungs, the bladder, the urethra and the auditory tube. It also forms the thyroid, thymus, gall bladder and pancreas. It improves assimilation, allergy problems and balances the parasympatheric nervous system.
C	1,168	Movement - Resonates with the middle tissue (the mesoderm) that forms connective tissue such as ligaments, tendons, cartilage, muscle and bone. It also forms the heart, blood and lymph vessels, kidneys, ovaries, testes, spleen and the cortex of the adrenal gland.
D	2,336	Coordination - Helps balance the two sides of the brain.
E	4,672	Nerves - Resonates with the spinal cord and peripheral nervous system.
F	73	Emotional Reaction - Resonates with the subcorticalor lower region of the brain, including the thalamus and hypothalamus, the two control centers of the body.

Lower EM Frequencies

Dr. Robert Becker documented the existence of an underlying electromagnetic life force within the body that stimulates it to grow and heal. His studies demonstrate that an injury causes the brain to send low-level, electrical signals to the wound that stimulates repair. As the repair process continues, this signal diminishes in intensity. The slower, stimulating signal, in turn, slows the repair activity, and when the wound heals, the signal stops.

Becker found if the current level is in a very low range one gets nerve regeneration. If it is much higher than that, one gets cell regeneration in the form of bone growth or ligament healing. This may explain the healing properties of relaxation, biofeedback, and meditation; all of which calm and slow the body down.

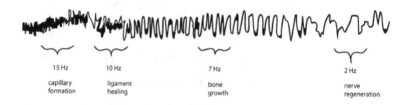

15 Hz
capillary
formation

10 Hz
ligament
healing

7 Hz
bone
growth

2 Hz
nerve
regeneration

Electromagnetic Life Force

Brain Waves

Electrical activity emanating from the brain is displayed in the form of brain waves. There are five categories of these brain waves, ranging from the most activity to the least activity. In the beta state, we are the most alert (our day consciousness) and this state is important for information processing and learning. This frequency of human brain activity is between

14 and 50 Hz. In the alpha state, with an electrical frequency between 8 to14 Hz, we are relaxed but alert.

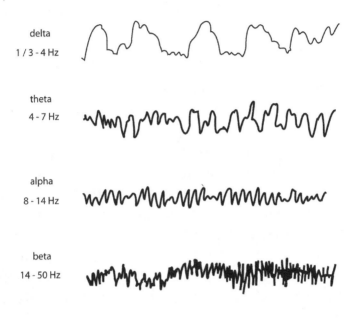

delta
1 / 3 - 4 Hz

theta
4 - 7 Hz

alpha
8 - 14 Hz

beta
14 - 50 Hz

EEG recorded brain waves

The theta state is one of drowsiness. It is a conscious state just before sleeping and just after waking and the state reached in meditation and is measured between 4 to 7 pulses per second. Delta brain waves are the slowest between 1-3 or 4 cycles per second. When asleep and dreaming, we have reached the delta state. These last two stages of brain activity are important for the healing and regeneration process.

In human electroencephalogram [EEG] studies, reflexology creates a relaxation response or puts the body in a theta state, a state in which it may begin the rejuvenation process and work to the best of its ability to heal itself. This was confirmed in EEG studies conducted by Dr. Jesus

Manzanares of Barcelona, who compared the changes in wave amplitudes with patients receiving reflexology. The EEG recorded waves that changed from alpha to theta and delta with the application of reflexology techniques.

Consciousness

Consciousness is the vital energy that both gives life to the body and survives beyond the body in a different realm of existence.

The discovery by Russian linguists that the genetic code in the apparently useless junk DNA that follows the same rules as all our human languages also points to the significance of sound frequencies and vibrations in the possibility that creation was generated by waves of consciousness.

By simply applying vibration and language points to the power of wave genetics, we come up with a greater influence on the formation of organisms than the biochemical processes of alkaline sequences.

Studies on thought and consciousness are emerging as fundamental aspects of disease and not as those unrelated to the usual course of the disease. These studies are leading to changes in the paradigms of biology and medicine. Science is increasingly agreeing we are more than the atoms and molecules of which we are composed, but beings that emit, communicate with, and are formed from the light of biophotons.

Intention Is a Living Force of Physiology

Even human intention itself may have an empirical basis in biophotons. Intention is defined as a directed thought to perform a determined action. Our intentions seem to operate as highly coherent frequencies capable of changing the molecular structure of matter in the quantum field. The mind transforms energy into thoughts. For the intention to be effective, it is necessary to choose the appropriate time.

We can't forget that there is also an energy that moves between the practitioner and the client and is a hidden aspect of the overall healing process. The role of intention in healing is a strong one. The synergy of anatomy and physiology combined with intention is more helpful in assisting the body to return to an optimal state of functioning. The use of intention is linked with our ability in our mind to visualize the proper function of the area of the body where our hands find areas of sensitivity.

Beyond our focused intention on anatomy and physiology we can use it to visualize the flow of energy. In this case, it can be a language to talk to the person and their subconscious is such a way the client effectively learns to reconnect to their own body, thoughts, emotions and spirit. In this way intention is used to communicate with, and influence, the life energy of the body. Engaged as conscious touch, intention connects with the tissues of the client's physical body and its life energy as well. In turn, energy responds to intention as energy flows where intention focuses.

Evolution to Quantum Energy

Energy not only surrounds us, it interpenetrates the cells of our body. The organs of our body are made of tissues made of cells, molecules, and atoms, which are all whirling, pulsating, vibrating fields of energy. All matter has vibration that, in turn, has a frequency. Within the body are different energy systems. On the gross or physical level (i.e., the physical level comprising the most dense level of energy), there are the biochemical and bioelectrical networks of the body as we have already discussed. In addition, there are higher, invisible energies or a life force responsible for life and creative expression beyond ordinary human perception.

In the 1980s, early studies in neuro-psychiatry demonstrated the interactions between chemical states and electromagnetic fields—that is, small, electric currents between specific brain points gave rise to the same behavioral changes observed with certain specific brain-stimulating chemicals.

The Tiller-Einstein Model attempts to describe the behavior of energy/matter at velocities beyond the speed of light in order to establish a reality base for subtle energies and subtle bodies—we will have more to say on this later. According to the Tiller-Einstein model, the energy/matter beyond the speed of light is electromagnetic in nature. The first level of energy moving faster than light is the etheric frequency of matter and energy in the subtle body surrounding us.

In 1983, Dr. William Tiller indicated that very low currents can modulate or balance the electromagnetics of current waves that are known as magnetic vector potential. Low currents, Tiller suggested, restores the vitality balance in organs by stimulating the body's magnetic vector potential. Tiller went on to postulate that slow-acting, low current, produce subtle changes on the cellular level in the body that can build up slowly and gradually to generate significant changes over time.

The bio-medical evolution, thanks largely to Einstein's (1879-1955) theory of relativity, $E=MC^2$ (Energy=Mass [matter] times C [a constant factor squared equaling the speed of light]), demonstrates that matter can be converted energy. This equation, published in 1905, laid the foundation of quantum mechanics in physics. Yet, it wasn't until 2019 that the equation was finally proven to be true.

Today it is better accepted that conventionally based medicine works with the biological energy fields of the body. With the acceptance of electrical and magnetic fields, it brings medicine slowly moving into the area of subtle, vibrational energy medicine. As a holistic discipline, reflexology addresses each individual as an entity of body, mind, emotions and spirit. It does not look symptomatically at the body but rather works with the whole person. Because the body is more than the sum of its anatomy, reflexology understands the client to be an integrated energy system.

Some natural therapies go further and are based on working at the subatomic level with the subtle energy/life force/healing energy surrounding the body. Some energy is detectible as frequencies within the electromagnetic spectrum, and others cannot be measured as yet. The equation now looks like this:

Function —> Structure —> Chemistry —> Electromagnetic fields —> $E=MC^2$
(physiology)<–(anatomy)<–(hormones) <—— (energy) <—— (subtle energies)*

*Energies that exist outside the ordinary space/time frame and move faster than light. Also known as subtle, vibrational energy medicine.

In conclusion, many forms of energy affect our life whether we understand them or not. Two hundred years ago, little was understood about electricity, but electric energy existed. Though scientifically unexplained, lightning struck, electric eels gave shocks, and the nervous system functioned. Even today, we may not fully understand how electricity works, although we use it routinely.

When we turn on a light, we don't need to understand how electrons travel back and forth in the wires. Neither do we need to be aware that for each of our thoughts and movements, the electrical energy that is our brain and nervous system has processed millions of messages. We don't need to know that each of those brain messages involves billions of complex exchanges of chemical energy into electrical energy. Instead, we have learned by experience how to make those forms of energy work for us in practical ways, even though we may not know how they work. We just raise our hand, flip the switch, and the light goes on.

This subtle invisible energy we are addressing that surrounds and flows in us is known in many cultures by different names. These include, but are not limited to, Chi/ TCM (China), Chakras/Prana of Ayurvedic medicine (India).

Subtle energy is also known as Qi or Ki (Japan), Manna (Hawaii/Polynesia), Pneuma (Greek mythology), Ka (Egyptian mythology), Ashe (African Yoruba mythology) and Num (Kalahari Desert).

No matter the name, all express the vibrational or life force of the human body surrounded by several levels of energy within an invisible energy system.

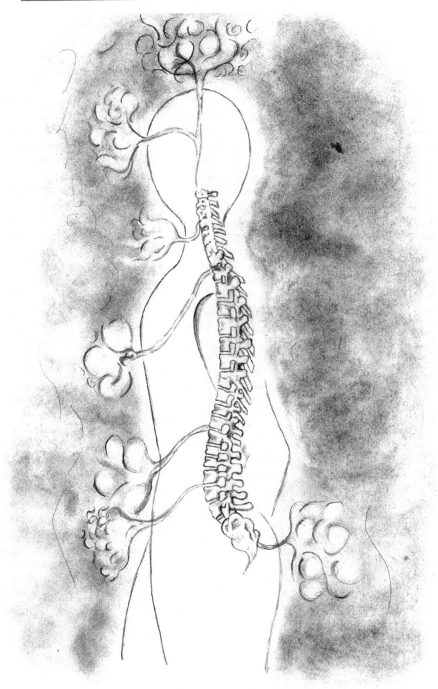

Chakras of Ayurvedic medicine

Chapter 4: HUMAN SUBTLE ENERGY SYSTEMS

In addition to the electrical and magnetic fields that surround everything physical, there are other types of energies and frequencies that are yet undetectable by instrumentation.

Thinking back to the example of the airplane propeller, subtle energy is a term referring to types of unseen matter of a higher frequency or vibration of matter.

Our physical body exists within a larger "body"; a human energy field or aura, which is the vibratory level through which we create our experience of reality, including our health and illness.

It is through this energy field that we have the power to heal ourselves.

Bioenergetics and Subtle Energy

Quantum physics tells us that matter and energy are two different manifestations of the same primary energetic substance of which everything in the universe is composed, including both our physical and subtle bodies. Bioenergetics is defined as any type of electrical, electromagnetic, or subtle energetic force that is generated by living organisms.

Energies of an electrical, electromagnetic and chemical nature have long been recognized by contemporary medicine. Subtle energy is a general term denoting energies that often exist outside the ordinary space/time frame and move faster than light. A gradation of these energies occurs and composes the four layers of energy surrounding each human being in what is called the aura. These are the levels of energy known to mystics or seen through clairvoyance.

Energy medicine involves the movement of energy, the mind, heart, and soul, plus the dynamics of the client-practitioner relationship. We "touch" people on many levels, not just the physical. The healing process itself is a mystery. The client-practitioner relationship—that is, how we work as practitioners out of our own being and in response to the needs of our clients—brings out our intuitive nature and encompasses the art of reflexology. Reflexology, to me, is not an intellectual activity but a sensory and intuitive one. The application of techniques and the intent of both the reflexologist and the client contribute to the healing process.

Through quantum physics, we no longer need to rely on mysticism to explain the workings of the body. There can be no argument that reflexology does assist in the movement of the energies in the body. The scientific ability to detect a potential health problem before it manifests may already be available. Technology to measure the electromagnetic disturbances in the meridian system of Traditional Chinese Medicine exists. Electrically unbalanced acupoints as diagnosed by this technology has the potential to detect pathology before it occurs. With a huge budget of research money some day we may prove this about reflexology too.

All matter, both physical and subtle, has a frequency. Matter of different frequencies can coexist in the same space, just as energies of different frequencies (i.e., radio and TV) can exist nondestructively in the same space. The greater "you" extends beyond the confines of your skin to reach and touch everywhere you can imagine and beyond into the unseen. Physically we are separate, but spiritually, in ways we may find hard to comprehend, not only are we connected but we're all one. In essence, this may be compared to different colors of the same light vibrating at different speeds that a prism breaks into a rainbow of colors.

When the mind is dominated by a negative worldview, the direct result is a repetition of minute changes in energy flow to the various body organs. The subtle field of overall physiology is affected in all of its complex functions—mediated by electron transfer, neural hormonal balance, nutritional status, and the like. Eventually, an accumulation of infinitesimal changes becomes discernible through medical tests. Unfortunately today, when these subtle changes are detected by conventional medicine, the disease process is already quite advanced.

In my view, reflexology is a blend of physical- and energy-based medicines. The conventional medicine is the bio-medical model and based on what can be seen, weighed and measured, while the energy model is based on the unseen.

Further adapting the Tiller formula, the phenomena would be:

Function ----->Structure ----->Chemistry ----->Electromagnetic fields ---> $E=MC^2$
(physiology)<—(anatomy) <—(hormones) <——— (energy) <----------(subtle
energies
of vibrational
medicine)

Physical and Subtle Energy Levels of Our Aura

The layer of matter that we see, hear, smell, touch, and taste is the only body visible to the naked eye. This outer body is linked to and surrounded by the other bodies of a higher vibratory rate.

Our subtle energy field is electromagnetic and interpenetrates our physical body with energy and is commonly referred to as our aura. Our aura is the holographic, energy matrix for our physical body of matter and the flow of energy in one form to another: energy flows from our inner bodies to create the matter of our physical body.

Our energy field being a radiation of electromagnetic energy extends both internally and externally, never ends, but sends out waves throughout the universe. It interacts with everything around us. Its strength weakens proportionally to the square of the distance, but there is no point at which you could say it stops. This living energy field can be photographed in a verifiable, repeatable way with instruments like the Kirlian camera. It reacts to our every thought, word, feeling, choice, and action instantly. Our aura is the energetic skin that holds all our inner energy bodies and outer body together.

The human energy field of our aura consists of various energetic layers or essentially various levels of energy vibrating at different speeds.

The subtle energetic expression of the multidimensional human being beyond the physical body includes the etheric or life body; the astral body, also known as the emotional body containing our emotions, feelings, soul and personality; the mental body of the body's innate intelligence encompasses our spirit or universal consciousness that connects us to the spiritual world.

Though often spoken of as higher or finer levels of energy and shown as layers, they actually penetrate one another and have an influence on each other.

In discussing the subtle energy-body connection, it is good to briefly define these levels so that we understand the use of words from a similar viewpoint. Four of the subtle energy bodies are defined below. Our bodies are composed of all three of these vibratory layers, plus our physical structure. In addition, there are three finer subtle energy levels of even higher frequencies that also contribute energies to the physical body that will not be addressed in this work.

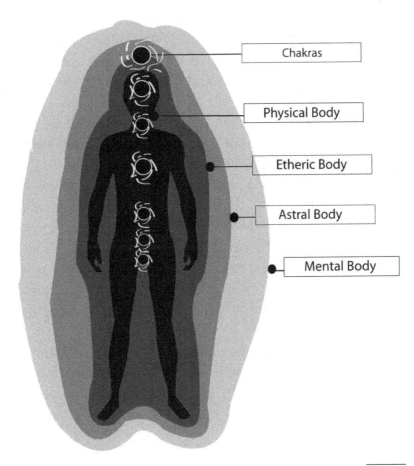

Chakras

Physical Body

Etheric Body

Astral Body

Mental Body

The Physical Body

In the subtle energy model, the physical body is the densest aspect. It is our material body; our anatomy and physiology; tactile sensations felt by the body. Touch is a component of our physical reflexology work. With the application of touch and pressure to the feet, hands, and outer ears, messages are sent to the brain by way of the nervous system and connective tissue (fascia) and elicit physical responses from the body, producing, amongst them, the relaxation process.

The physical body cannot heal by itself. Yes, it can affect tissue repair, but it does not necessarily heal pain, which is invisible, or let go of the trauma of the injury, which can have an emotional base. The emotional body may heal, and we may feel hope and unconditional love, or experience the release of anger, fear, or sadness and other negative sentiments, but again, this alone is not enough to heal the body.

The mind is powerful, but it alone cannot heal the body. I contend that when all four of our subtle bodies come into alignment through the relaxation process, healing occurs. This begins with a change of thought process (mental body involvement), a change in attitude (emotional body connection) and allows the physical body to express these changes. When the spiritual level is involved, miracles may occur. Nevertheless, to be healed, there must be a synergistic involvement of the four aspects of our nature. Caring touch is the mediating factor that has the potential of bringing about this synchronicity.

In experiencing reflexology, the subtle bodies are brought into alignment. This allows the client temporary relief of symptoms and lets him or her experience the potential of healing that can occur. For a few minutes, hours or days, a window of opportunity opens that allows the client to unconsciously, or consciously, experience what life can be like without his or her condition.

Do you recall Eunice Ingham's often-repeated statement that circulation (movement) is life and stagnation is death? We are always in the state of creation. With the application of touch and pressure to the feet, hands and or outer ears messages are sent to the brain by way of the nervous system and elicit a physical response from the body. Our cells change shape, move, grow, and "choose" what to do based on movement. Consider that one stiff muscle can change the structure of our whole body. Our bodies need to move or be moved to keep our tissues healthy and flexible.

Reflexology assists in bringing our bodies into balance by aiding our circulation, helping us sort out our thoughts and feelings, and enhancing our energy and encouraging letting go of patterns that no longer serve us. In this way, relaxation occurs. And according to Ayurveda medicine, the state of relaxation is the first step in healing. The stress-reducing, biochemical and energetic environment induces healing through the autonomic nervous system and promotes the body to balance itself as optimally as it is able.

Etheric (Life Body)

The body nearest the physical body is the etheric or life body. This is a system of energy not physically visible to external sight. The etheric is a finer duplicate of the physical body and gives it "life." It extends two inches beyond the skin. In life, it is never separated from the physical body and disintegrates with the body at death. When a physical organ is removed, there still remains in the etheric body the inner vital activity that would be carried on by the body part that was removed.

The history of the painful trauma inflicted to the body by surgery, well-intentioned or not, or by a dramatic physical accident, is remembered by the body until it is released. This blocked energy can result in being expressed as phantom limb pain. The etheric body contains the energy channels called the chakras and nadis of Ayurveda medicine.

Astral (Emotional Body)

The sentimental, sensitive nature of our feelings, our personality and ego is part of the subtle energy of the astral body. In psychological terms, it is our sense of self and expressed as "I."

In the aura the astral body extends four to five inches from the body's surface. Emotions or thoughts colored by feelings are part of our life and the healing process. No physical experience is unaccompanied without an emotional response and mental interpretation.

Today, psychologists acknowledge the effect feelings have upon physical health and behavior. Feelings are part of the mind-body connection. Emotional imbalance may manifest itself when we allow ourselves to be drained by the demands of others and by the unrealistic demands we place on ourselves. A key here is to validate our true feelings in ourselves and others.

According to Dr. Christine Page of England, "Tests have shown when this is done, the immune system reacts positively even if the emotions expressed are so-called negative ones, anger, grief, etc. If the four core emotions [fear, anger, sadness, joy] are not appropriately expressed when they are experienced, within five days they can become a chronic problem, which is then much harder to release." She goes on to say, "Fear can transform to anxiety or worry; sadness can lead to despair or depression and even joy can become stuck in the person wanting to please others by being continually cheerful."

A challenge often faced by reflexologists is how to help with the release of tension at the mental-emotional levels as well as the physical. Through the dialogue between practitioner and client, a fresh point of view may emerge and bring hope and relief from anxiety and stress. This, in turn, can bring on the change in behavior or thinking necessary for healing. To establish this relationship, the client must participate in discussions, which include exchanges of ideas, rather than simply receiving instructions or information from the practitioner. When the client becomes active in the process by assuming her share of responsibility toward her health, a positive attitude can be attained and sustained.

On the physical level, explains reflexologist Barbara Mosier of Colorado, "Emotions operate from the endocrine glands of the body. Messages are sent from these glands to the autonomic and cerebrospinal nervous systems affecting the body's physiology. Positive emotions create positive responses in the body by maintaining and building health. On the other hand, negative emotions and negative habits, even in an unconscious state, create a disturbance in the way the body systems are able to function, giving an open door to the state of dis-ease."

Our emotions are the mind-body bridge. As a result, an emergence of emotions is a vital part of healing. Emotions, as currents of energy with different frequencies, when allowed to pass through us by the touch of the practitioner, may bring about an emotional relaxation and release of stress on this level.

This aspect of the emotional body extends eight to ten inches away from the body. When close relationships are involved, aspects of this layer will be 12-18 inches from the skin. Once emotions are recognized, the energy formerly used to block them can then be used by the body in healing or balancing itself.

As practitioners we must also be aware of our own emotional messages that are communicated to the client silently through our touch, tactile skills, our voice, our attitude toward life, our intentions, and in many other ways.

Mental Body (Mind or the Body's Innate Intelligence)

Reference here is not to the brain but to the mind or the innate intelligence of the body that is in every cell. The brain is a mass of tissue that is the main part of the nervous system. It is understood to be the organ that receives sensory impulses and regulates motor impulses. The physical brain is often confused with the mind and incorrectly credited with being the center of thought. It is not the originator of consciousness but rather its instrument. This layer is found two to two and a half feet from the body.

The mind controls the autonomic nervous system; our intellect and thoughts; the reasoning part of our nature. The mind interprets and translates the complex changes in our environment and the things that happen to us. As soon as we feel something, we rationalize that feeling and place it in the context of our experience, so that our emotions and thoughts are constantly interacting. For instance, the heart as a muscle cannot decide to feel the loss of a loved one. The stomach does not perceive that a work situation is bad. The immune system does not know whether its owner just lost a job or a spouse. The brain does not recognize any of these scenarios, but the mind does. The mind "thinks" and programs the computer known as our brain.

The human mind is in charge of managing our health. Health is influenced by our social worlds, mental and emotional lives, and internal physiology. Psychological and social factors interpreted by the mind can influence our immunity from infectious and other diseases. Relaxation of the mind eases tension and creates space for healing to occur.

While mental factors cannot account for all illness, the importance of mental attitudes and brain function are often overlooked by conventional medicine. Until the late 20th century and the advent of the integrative health movement, the importance of the patient's mind in healing was largely ignored. The influence of grief, despair, or discouragement on the onset and outcome of illness were not taken into account. Neither were the effects of faith, confidence, and peace of mind on the ability to heal.

Effects of Focused Intent on the Mental Level

Returning to the effects of focused intent this time as encouragement, it can stimulate the client's body defenses against disease. Through the words of the practitioner and the client's interaction, the client's body responds directly to positive thoughts. Encouragement in this instance does not mean lying to the client but, instead, offering support and hope. Hope comes in many ways. When it comes from the client's confidence and trust in the practitioner, it is established through the client-practitioner bond. An atmosphere filled with humor and love will help develop this bond.

When working on the client, the practitioner, as a lay helper, could try to discover what the client is thinking and feeling— what the client perceives her problems to be—through asking questions and actively listening. The reflexologist can inspire the patient's confidence by listening more than talking.

Frequently, it is amazing to me as I am working on someone what bubbles up and is expressed by the client without my having to probe or forcing conversation on a certain topic.

Our capacity to understand, forgive, and accept is directly linked to our personal health. We could say that the invisible universe of thought and attitude becomes visible as a consequence of the body's habitual response. External events may define conditions, but they do not determine the consciousness level of recovery from any disease process. Healing is dependent upon our willingness to explore new ways of looking at our response to situations. Love, compassion, and forgiveness, which may be mistakenly seen by some as submissive or a weakness, are, in fact, empowering.

Change is difficult, uncomfortable, and often frightening. A change in thought process produces a chemical change in the body, which can be the beginning of the healing process. Change, we know, may not always be an easy or a quick process. Our clients need to know we stand with them without judgment to assist them through change. Perhaps a suggestion will instill in the client the possibility for change if it is feasible for her to change and if she gives up the need to control, because in reality, the only person we have control over is our self. We cannot control how others will react to us. We must learn to like whom we are or change into someone we like. When that occurs, we can control the stress from external pressures.

It should be noted that beyond positive thinking, reflexology works without focused intent, for it works with the innate intelligence of the client's body that knows where the healing energy is needed most. Although the life force is affected by our thoughts, it is not essential to concentrate, meditate, or attempt in any way to influence the client's body. That is the responsibility of the client's innate intelligence.

The thought most helpful to the client is that the highest good of all concerned be the outcome.

The Mental Body as Our Higher Self

The mind is often referred to as our "Higher Self," or soul and has no physical or material reality. The soul is the individual, energetic, or essence, that is unique to each of us and shapes our life on earth. Our higher self is our sense of the universal vibrational field, of universal energetic consciousness, universal truth, or our ethical beliefs, and is not religious in nature. This level is made up of all the energy around us, including nature and the cosmos.

It is the eternal core of our being and that part of our makeup connected to a higher source of wisdom. This connection may be strengthened through prayer and meditation. It holds the answers to our deepest questions and may also be accessed through applied kinesiology or other means. To the person seeing auras this level extends three feet from the body.

Spiritual Growth and Our Beliefs

We create our boundaries based on our beliefs. We come into this life knowing the Universal Truth. As we grow up, we disconnect from the universal truth and inherit our family's belief system. Our parents' beliefs usually end up being the foundation of our beliefs. The foundation of this belief creates our restrictions. These boundaries may come to limit our spiritual growth or inner development, which affect our cells and DNA and vice versa. This explains why two individuals living in the same environment can draw to themselves vastly different subtle energies based on their core beliefs. These differences could then significantly affect both their perceptions of "reality" and what they deemed to be possible, as well as what they might actually be able to accomplish within those perceived "realities." Only in taking time for self-reflection and questioning our beliefs can we determine our own reality.

To inspire implies filling with spirit; dispirited means dejected, hopeless, defeated. Spirit equates with life; the energy of life itself can be termed spirit. It is the expression of alignment with life's energy. Self-realization and soul awakening requires expansion of our existing beliefs beyond the restrictions of our programmed belief system.

Ultimately, each health challenge is an opportunity to increase one's consciousness. Life is challenging. There are no mistakes or problems, only opportunities to learn. We have the power to see every situation as a learning experience contributing to our personal growth. Revenge, judgment and condemnation, regardless of moral righteousness, is of a lower vibrational level.

The ultimate choices in life are whether to align with a higher energy or lower energy. Very rarely is the easy way the correct choice for spiritual growth.

Chapter 5: UNDERSTANDING THE HUMAN ENERGY FIELD

Subtle energy is where ancient wisdom and modern science meet. In the western scientific world, the body ends at the surface of the skin. This is a limited view. Surrounding each of us, as we have discussed, is an electromagnetic, subtle energy field extending further than the skin. The ancient sages, through direct perception, knew of this information about subtle energies that we are slowly rediscovering. This life force is a subtle form of electromagnetic energy. As noted above, it has been called by many different names in many cultures. It can be thought of as a circulating energy field surrounding and penetrating the body. It is an animating current of life and is naturally directed by the body's intelligence. When the subtle electromagnetic fields around the body are balanced, the nerves of the parasympathetic nervous system are relaxed.

Quantum physicists have been telling us for a some time that everything, including our bodies, is, at its most basic level, pure energy. Physicist Barbara Brennan has actually proven the existence of a multi-level human energy field, also known as the aura. Her work bridges science and spirituality. As an atmospheric physicist, Brennan, a former research scientist for NASA, is one of the first scientists to study and prove in depth the existence of the human energy field and its connection to a person's health and well-being, and discussed how to work with this field to affect physical and emotional "dis-ease."

Brennan's teacher was Rosalyn L. Bruyere, an internationally acclaimed healer and clairvoyant who was also originally trained as an engineer. Bruyere was instrumental in the eight-year research on the human electromagnetic field conducted at UCLA in collaboration with Dr. Valerie Hunt. They conducted numerous research projects using electrodes to study the human energy field. The two scientists were able to measure the frequencies of the human energy field and proved that these frequencies correlated with the frequencies of visible light. In essence, we are vibrational energy beings composed of light and sound energy.

Our aura is the vital life force that makes us alive and interconnected with all life. It houses our internal energy meridians in the body of Traditional Chinese Medicine and the chakras of Ayurvedic medicine. It is an egg-shaped interwoven strands of energy that manifest as light. The colors of the aura are in constant motion, and every picture created to illustrate the aura can only be an approximation of what is seen **at that moment**. The body's responses shift and change from instant to instant in reaction to one's train of thought and emotions that, in turn, creates change in the colors and shape of the aura. Thus the aura is filled with energy patterns that determine the health of a person.

Our energy field is the instrument of wellness and the source of illness. Disease starts in the aura, on some level caused by blockages in the energy flow. If the disturbances are not cleared at that the subtle energy level, eventually the disease manifests in the physical body.

Barbara Brennan said it best: "It is essential that we deal with the deeper meaning of our illnesses. We need to ask, what does this illness mean to me? What can I learn from this illness? Illness can be seen as simply a message from your body to you that says: 'Wait a minute: something is wrong. You are not listening to your whole self; you are ignoring something that is very important to you.' A return to health requires more personal work and change than simply taking pills prescribed by a doctor. Without personal change, you will eventually create another problem to lead you back to the source that caused the disease in the first place."

Our auric patterns can come from this life or can be carried over from prior existence(s). Stored patterns consist of dis-empowering thought forms, traumas, stress, beliefs, etc. These patterns can cause physical, mental, emotional, and spiritual disconnections. Healing these energy patterns in a timely manner can prevent these inner patterns from manifesting as outer illness and disease.

Auras and Reflexology

I have first-hand, empirical evidence to support the concept of subtle energy fields of the body and the movement of energy with reflexology. I have a daughter with the ability to see auras—not just around the head as in the picture of saints but the entire body. Today, she would be called a medical intuitive. About 35 years ago, when she was young, I asked her to work with me to verify what I intuitively thought was happening during a session. I did not want to influence her in any way, so I didn't disclose to her what I thought or sensed was happening. What follows is a sampling of her work.

Being eight years old, my daughter did not have the patience to fill in the bands of color. She simply drew the line of color once without enlarging it. She explained that the colors really appeared like the colors we see in a rainbow. That is, in fuzzy bands with one color blending seamlessly into the next on either side.

In all these drawings, you will notice the aura is not next to the body. While not drawn, this is the space in which the etheric or life body is located. The etheric body extends about two to four inches out from the skin and in shape is a duplicate of the physical body. Immediately my daughter complained the colors of the pencils she had to work with were not "right." We went to a larger set of artist colored pencils. These, she said, although better were still not correct, as the colors she saw were not seen in the physical world, but she'd do the best she could. She also complained the paper was too small. We then went to 8x14 sized paper and a single outline of either the front or back on each page.

I did not ask my daughter to interpret what the colors meant to her as they vary from observer to observer. I also did not want this to be an intellectual activity but simply a recording of what she was seeing.

My daughter did pick up on the energy level of the client. Once she was so tired she didn't want to draw; she wanted to rest her head on the desk. Another time, the client was so excited about an upcoming trip to Europe, my daughter told her to calm down as her aura was so big it wouldn't fit on the page.

Client One

This was the first client in our study and subsequent results. Without being asked my daughter proceeded to draw the areas where the body was holding tension before a session. To my surprise, areas that were holding tension that I visualized as being inflamed and red in color and predominantly round in shape weren't. Instead, the shape of where tension was held in the body and sentitivity was found by my hands, was not uniform and was multi-colored. The client then sat again after the session. The blackened areas are those that were no longer holding tension. Later in our anecdotal study, the areas that changed were circled, not blackened out.

At this particular session the client, unbeknownst to my daugher, complained of hypoglycemia, low thyroid, headache in the forehead, fatigue, knee stiffness and stomach tension.

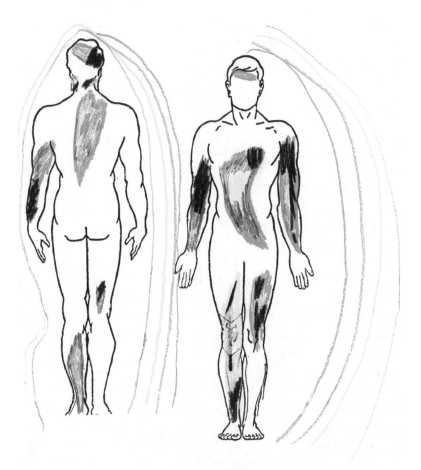

These two pages show Client One again before and after another session with the same complaints. The tension areas and shape of the aura has changed. At this particular session the very faint but visible yellow lines on top of the aura above the head and under the feet can be seen. They are unique, and indicative of the mental body which was not often drawn by my daughter.

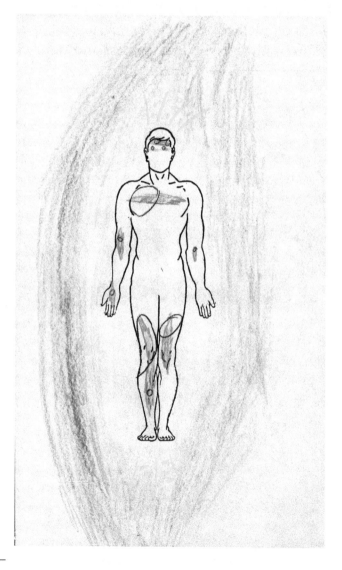

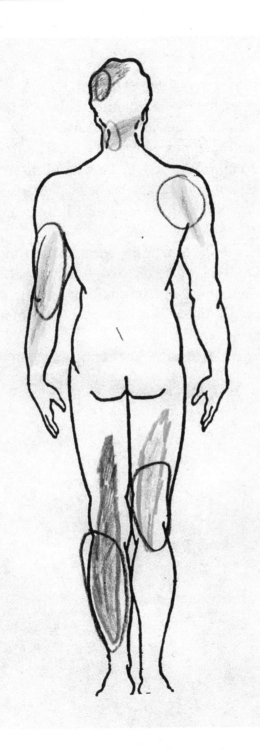

Client Two

It is important to remember that prints in books showing the aura are not a true representation of the colors or the shape of an aura. An aura does not necessarily consist of solid bands of color and may not be egg-shaped. The front and back of the person may be different. This stands to reason when you think of the anatomy of the body. The anterior and posterior muscles are different, in addition, all tissue and organs have a front and back.

Different objects may be seen inside the aura by some clairvoyants. As a general rule, we found the colors in the auras always changed from muddy to clear and sometimes with more positive colors replacing those of a less vibratory rate after a session.

On the next two pages are examples of auras with unusual shapes.

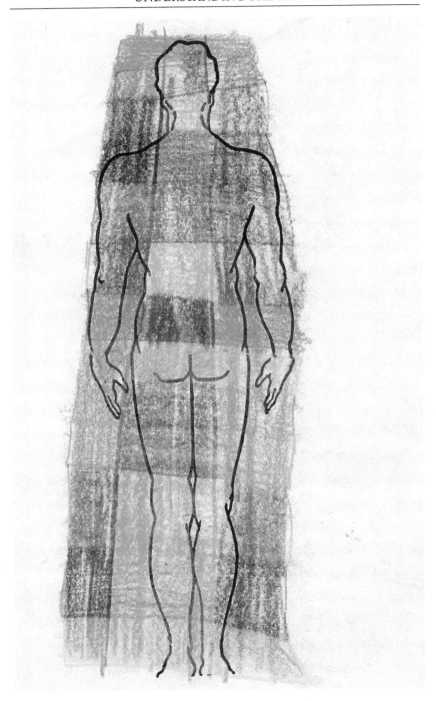

Client Three

It is interesting to note no aura was drawn around the head or feet.

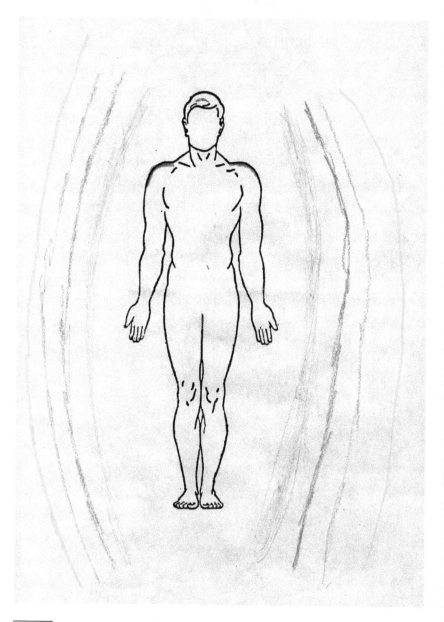

Client Four

This is Client Four before the first session.

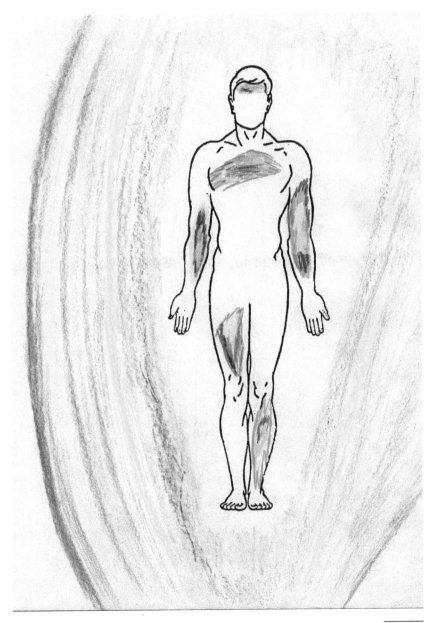

Client Four - The Back Before Session

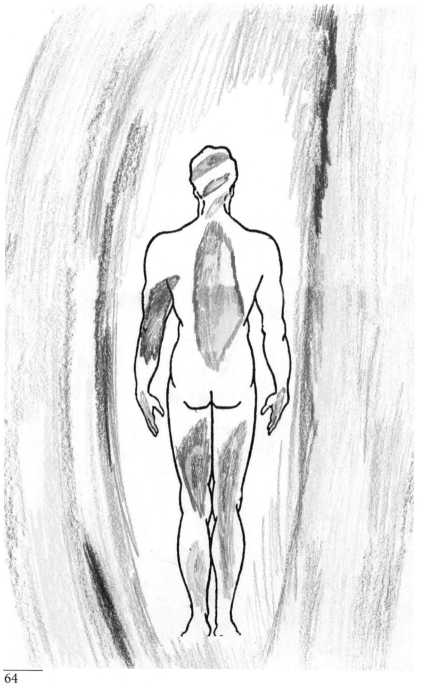

Client Four - After Session 2 Weeks Later

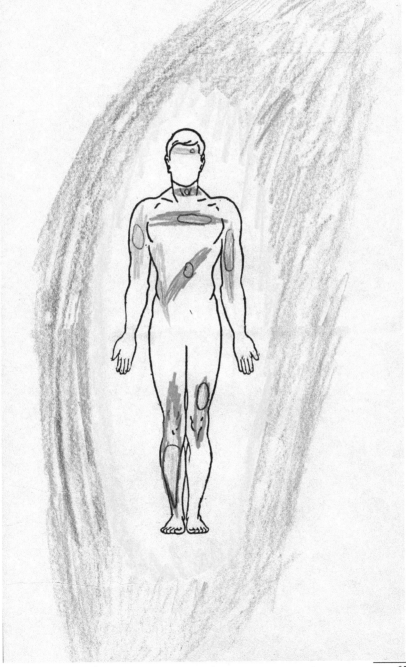

Client Five -Before & After

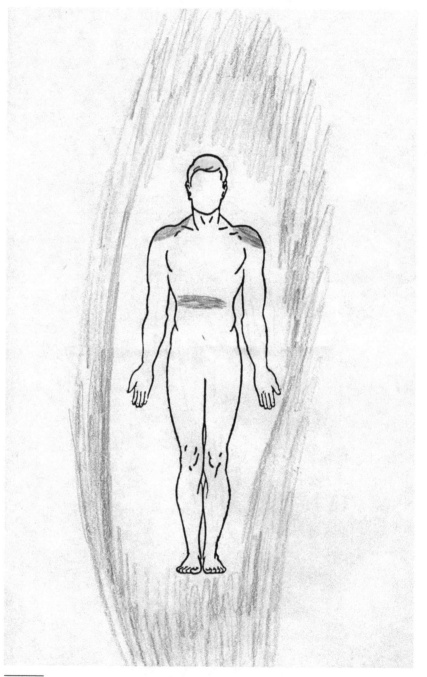

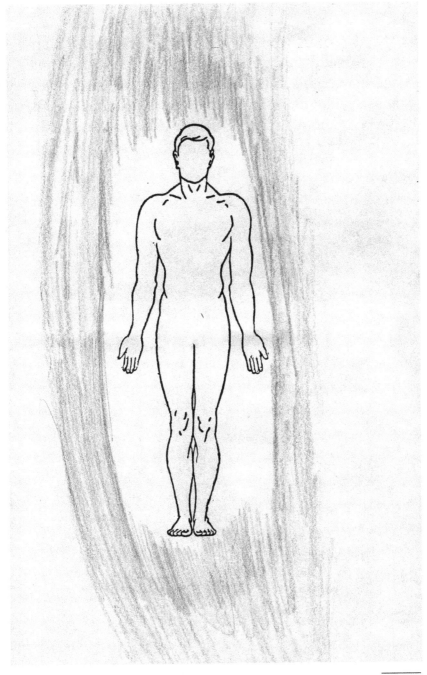

Client Six

The darkness here is not positive. This lower vibrational energy could indicate a serious problem lies ahead unless the energy is released. The closer to the body the negative energy appears, the more immediate the problem will manifest in the body. In this case the client was depressed. She had just suffered the death of her 11 months old son.

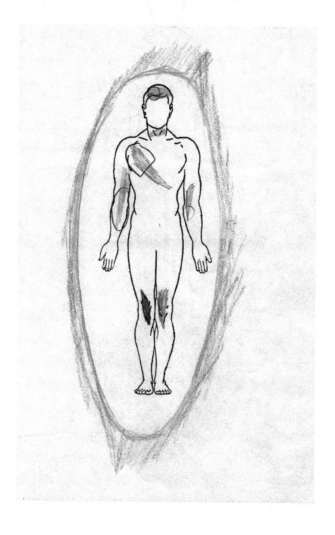

Client Seven

These two drawings are before and after the first session. On this day "sparkles" are recorded above the head in front and back. The colors of the aura change dramatically and have shape. The more vibrant colors suggest increased vitality and energy with the relaxation process.

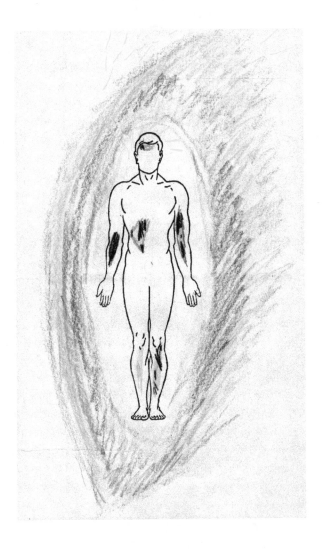

Client Seven - After

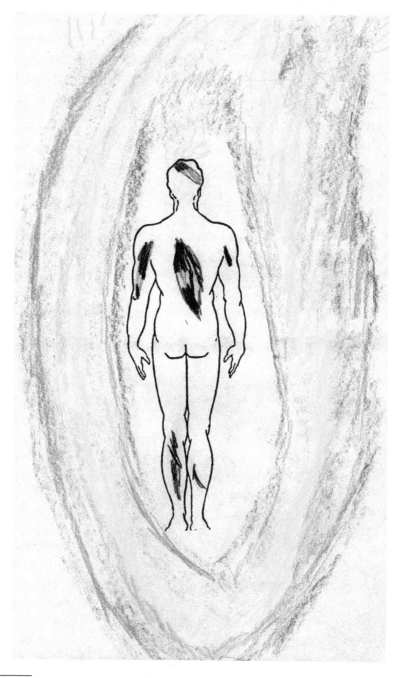

Client Seven before session two months later with no sessions between it and the initial session.

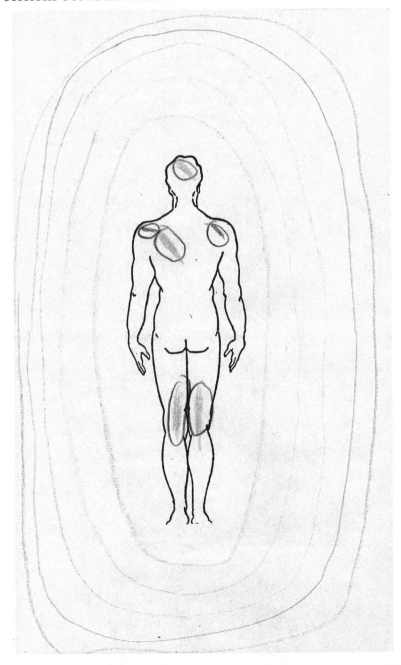

Client Seven, six weeks after the last session. The front before profile indicates tension in the shoulders, head and a little in the knees. After the session, little tension is left in the shoulders. Again the shape and colors in the aura changed dramatically.

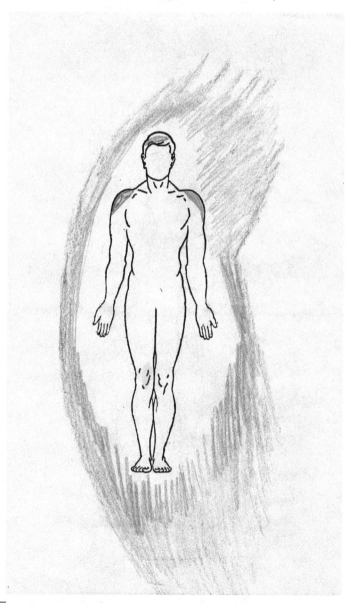

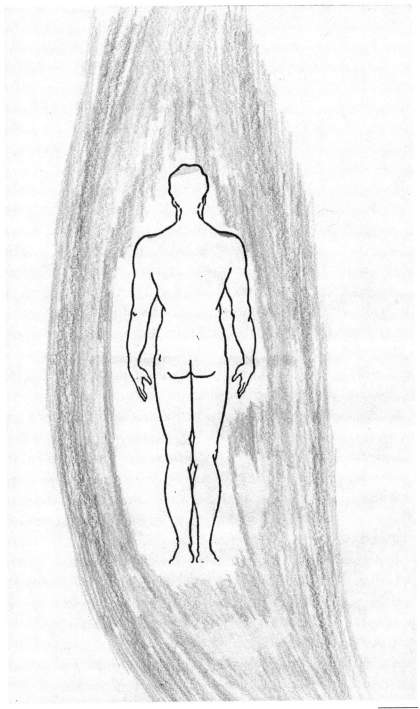

Relevance of Auras and Reflexology

The relevance of this energy concept is that techniques will not necessarily make us a better practitioner—it is the quality of our touch that is the most important element. In addition, it is not where we are touching so much as the movement of energy; whether or not we believe in this concept, it still exists and is active.

After a session, what we termed the "sore spots" or sensitive areas changed in shape, colors, and intensity or disappeared altogether. Those located on areas I hadn't touched, like the upper arm and thighs, changed also, proving to me that reflexology has a systemic effect on all areas on the body, so it wasn't just through touch to a particular area that produces change in the body. Was this occurring through the nervous system, the circulatory system, or the subtle energy bodies? It seems, at the very least, to be all three.

It was also noteworthy that over a number of sessions, the changes remained permanent or continued to improve. Don't you find that as sessions continue on a consistent basis, most clients improve?

I don't see auras, but intuitively, as I'm working with someone, I feel it is not my energy being used but energy from a higher source, and my aura is being cleansed as the energy passes through me to my hands to the client. I asked my daughter what was happening in my aura. Was it being cleansed? To which she replied, "Oh, Mom, yours just begins to sparkle," thus verifying to me that the change I felt does occur and demonstrating that reflexology is a win-win situation—and why I often felt better after a session too.

As we conducted our experiment over three months, my daughter's abilities grew. She was able to draw what the aura would be after a session before I even touched the client. Or given a date in time, she was able to go back to that day and describe what the person's aura was like. She could also look at a photo and see the auras of those present.

Some of the participants were fascinated with what was drawn and pressed for an interpretation or a "reading." My daughter did not want this responsibility as she intuitively knew what she drew at that moment was only a record of the potential of what could occur. At eight, she didn't have the vocabulary or psychological knowledge to articulate that what she saw need not occur. She felt if she expressed it, the client would take on the illness. Yet, it was at the client's discretion to accept or not what was being shown and do the work (of which my daughter didn't know what that was) to move the negative energy away and out of their aura.

At such a young age my daughter didn't have training in how to control seeing things and was open to the impressions all the time. She witnessed (or saw things) that frightened her. Eventually, all of this proved to be a heavy burden and she didn't want to continue with our experiment or to see auras at all, so I honored her wishes and we stopped.

My Sessions

The way I visualize illness being created is through stress—it doesn't matter whether the cause is physical, environmental, mental, or emotional—the various subtle energetic bodies are directly layered on top of each other. Through stress, these bodies are pulled out of alignment. Healing cannot occur if any one or more of these bodies is out of place. With the relaxation response, the subtle layers of the body become congruent again, and the door to healing is opened. This makes the stress reduction or relaxation process the most powerful model of reflexology practice.

I prefer to work on a table or bed as that seems to be the most relaxing for the client. Though this may not be true, in my mind working with the client in a chair puts a crimp in the circulation of the energies at the pelvic region.

Some reflexologists believe a session should be quiet to produce the greatest level of relaxation. No talking, and definitely there should be no discussion about politics or religion. However, my sessions are rarely quiet. They are a combination of talking and silence. I find there are thoughts within clients, and the client may not know what will bubble up during a session, that they need to express in a safe, nonjudgmental environment, and by expressing these, an energy shift occurs that, in turn, creates peace within the mind and tranquility within the soul, and opens the door for healing. Once again, this goes back to reflexology assisting in the movement of the energies of the body.

Usually, in the first half of a session, while the client is on their back there is dialogue as the client "unloads," as I work on their feet and hands. The unloading is non-scripted, and the client and I are often surprised at what surfaces and needs to be aired. There is something about thoughts being kept hidden, in the dark, if you will, that allows them to fester. Bringing them out into the light makes the perceptions more manageable and less threatening.

Next I have the client turn over to lay on their stomach while I work on their feet and leg from that direction. I find I often discover sensitivity in areas I didn't find at first. This half of the session is usually quiet as the client gives into the relaxation process. During the last part of a session I have the client return to laying on their back again as I reflex their face and outer ears. Working on the ears last has a profoundly relaxing effect overall bringing total relaxation to the muscular system.

I frequently work with my eyes closed. I "see" better when I eliminate the distraction of my surroundings and then I am able to concentrate on what my hands are telling me. For example, when experiencing heat or tightness in tissue with no sensitivity in the surrounding tissue this often indicates congestion is present in that area and needs to be worked out. Or if I find sensitivity and go back to work on the area and find the feeling greatly diminished or gone it means the complex tissue in the foot was implicated and has relaxed as opposed to a specific reflex involvement. When sensitivity if found overall in the majority of the foot it appears to me and indication the body is storing superficial tension in the whole body.

When I find myself yawning or coughing it is an indication the client is freeing herself of disturbed energy and I don't need to hold it in my body. The yawning and coughing are a positive indication my body is releasing this unwanted energy.

Working With Children

It has been my experience that this process is the same for children and teens, even with my own children. As a parent, reflexology was a blessing as my children were growing up. It allowed me to find out what issues they were dealing with without my getting into their space and prying it out of them. First, I always made them make an appointment like everyone else. In this way, they were honoring reflexology, me as a reflexologist, and my time. Again, it was interesting what they would talk about during a session. In the space created, they felt safe to express their concerns or struggles— which, again, they often were not consciously aware of at the beginning of a session. I was no longer their mother, but a nonjudgmental and compassionate third party. As with any client, it was not my responsibility to provide solutions, only the space for healing.

Sharing Stories

Something else that works for me with clients is sharing stories with them about what is going on or has gone on in my life, challenges I faced and how I've addressed them, or my personal truth about something. This is not done in a dictatorial manner but providing another way for the client to view a situation. Usually, the topic of what I share is based on an intuitive level or triggered in response to something the client has shared. As I'm sharing, my mind may say, "Why am I sharing this story? It is silly." It seems this is a way to open the door for the client's own disclosures of what is bothering them. Often, a person may not respond to what I express but, when she goes to leave, will say, "That's just what I needed to hear! I got the message."

I am astounded! I am not clairvoyant and contribute this to divine guidance, and I have had to learn to accept my own intuition. Talking also lets my hands work naturally as I'm not focused on "thinking" about what I am doing physically and they move to areas most needing work.

Booking The Next Session

When clients ask when they should return for maintenance, I explain the need for them to listen to their own body. For one of my clients, it is when his voice reaches a certain pitch. For another, it is when he notices tension in a specific muscle in his back. For a third, it is when she experiences nightmares; for another client, when life begins to look gray and there's little joy; and for a fifth client, when her PMS lasts longer than a few days before her cycle begins.

I leave it up to the client when to call for an appointment. This isn't a good business practice, but I do not want to plant a subconscious thought that the client needs to see me in a specific timeframe. By listening to their body, clients assume responsibility regarding the timing for a return appointment; this could be longer or shorter than I would have advised. The only time I make a recommendation for a return visit is when we are working on an acute problem; for example, a sudden problem in the back, and the relaxation process only partially occurs on the physical level with the initial visit. Then it is best to see the client again fairly soon, within a few days, so we can continue the relaxation process as opposed to starting all over again in a week or so.

TM *1999 Alonzo Bartley*

Chapter 6: ANATOMY OF CONSCIOUSNESS

Consciousness is seen by many in the metaphysical field as a type of energy. The anatomy of consciousness produces a profile of the entire human being—the seen, the unseen, the emotional and spiritual developments of the individual. Consciousness is often defined as the state of being aware, mentally awake—that is, not asleep. It also means what is known or felt by one's inner self or higher mental life of which a person is aware.

Consciousness is the vital energy that both gives life to the body and survives beyond the body in a different realm of existence. Consciousness takes many forms, and it ranges beyond what we ordinarily think of as the conscious mind into the refined dimensions of the highest energies. States of consciousness are actual conditions that are different from one another but not separate—either from each other or from the body itself. This can be likened to the experience of listening to music. Each note and instrument has its range of frequencies, but they all play a part in creating the song. Likewise, the subtle energy fields all work closely together as indicated in our aura.

Our subconscious mind is not physically located in our brain. It springs from our spiritual self. It moves us in the direction of possibilities; of our dreams. The actions taken or not taken reveal our thoughts that are believed in the most or least. By taking action, we demonstrate where our true beliefs lie and where our thinking is. Actions are our beliefs in motion, linking the present to the future. We automatically act in line with our beliefs.

The decision-making process is a function of consciousness itself; the mind makes choices based on millions of pieces of data and their correlations and projections, far beyond conscious comprehension, and with enormous rapidity. We think we must react to the physical, instead of coming into alignment with the spiritual side of our life. The physical world is a mirror of our own beliefs and thoughts, which means that if there are any appearances we'd like to change, we must think first by going within.

Intuition

We're all highly creative, yet we often don't allow our own creativity to flow because of the limiting beliefs we possess. We do not have to exclusively use logic to figure out the tasks and challenges before us. Intuition comes through to us as creatively thinking. For this to occur, our thinking must be open as we suspend our reliance on rational thinking, or the methodical brain.

Intuition is a level of consciousness that is beyond the mind and gives us insights beyond our knowledge and provides us inspiration. Using our intuition makes it possible for us to see new truths or to find creative solutions to problems and to make sudden leaps in understanding—those aha moments experienced in life.

Our intuition originates outside our normal awareness— not from outside ourselves but from within, independent of the physical world. Our intuition draws on our unconscious knowledge and is brought forth to our conscious mind when the need arises as an inspiration. Sometimes an answer may present itself, and by tracing the thought back, we can find the source of the inspiration and the rationale for our intuition.

Our Psychic Ability

It has often been said we are all psychic to some extent. Some develop the ability to see auras through years of work; others, like my daughter, are simply born with that ability. Our psychic senses interact with the subtle energies that cannot be discerned physically or measured by current technology. There are many books on exploring this subject. However, for our work with reflexology, it is not necessary to be psychic or to see auras.

Applied Kinesiology

Applied kinesiology is one way to test for congestion in the body, and you don't have to be psychic to do it. Kinesiology is another name for muscle testing that can be likened to dowsing. Muscle testing was developed in the 1960s by chiropractor George Goodheart. He created a system in which it is possible to tap into the innate intelligence of the client's body to reveal answers to the source of challenges the client is dealing with. Goodheart discovered that there was a relationship with the meridians and major organs, in addition to the muscles. He called his system Applied Kinesiology.

Applied kinesiology is not used to diagnose, treat or work with diseases. It accesses and enhances the body's innate healing ability. Techniques have been developed in applied kinesiology to test many areas of the body as well as how the body is affected by food and other substances. Kinesiology is also used to determine how well one handles emotional, mental and spiritual stress. It can help identify blockages and to balance a person.

Books have been written on the subject validating its use, with the most authoritative being *Power vs. Force* by David Hawkins, M.D., Ph.D. Dr. Hawkins, who worked as a psychiatrist, uses theoretical concepts from particle physics, nonlinear dynamics, and chaos theory to support his study of human behavior and how anyone may determine truth from lies of any statement using applied kinesiology. Consciousness, he posits is a global function dominated by the energy patterns that the new science of nonlinear dynamics terms attractors.

Applied kinesiology works like a computer; the body's consciousness or innate intelligence simply answers true or false, to a question. Similar to applied kinesiology, a pendulum may also be used to obtain yes or no answers to any question.

According to Hawkins, any ambiguities in the process are introduced by the questioning method, not the answering mechanism. Precision in asking questions is of paramount importance. Questions have to be very carefully defined: What we think is good or bad is merely subjective; what the universe or our higher self "thinks" about it may be something else entirely.

It's said that the question and the answer are merely two sides of the same coin, and that one can't pose a question unless the answer already exists—otherwise there would be no pattern that the question could be formulated from.

Hawkins has also charted and calibrated the vibrational rate for certain emotions, the truth of information found in various media presentations, and the collective level of consciousness of society.

In regards to health and healing Hawkins says, "The human central nervous system clearly has an exquisitely sensitive capacity to differentiate between life-*supportive* and life-*destructive* patterns. ...[E]nergy patterns, which make the body go strong, release brain endorphins and have a tonic effect on all of the organs; adverse stimuli release adrenaline, which suppresses immune response and instantaneously causes both weakness and even breakdown of specific organs, depending on the nature of the stimulus. Physiologically speaking, in choice of attitude, one chooses between anabolic endorphins or catabolic adrenaline. "

He goes on to state, "This clinical phenomenon forms the basis for such treatments as chiropractic, acupuncture, reflexology, and many others. These therapies, however, are usually designed to correct the *results* of an energy imbalance, but unless the attitude that's causing the energy imbalance is corrected, the illness tends to return."

While we, as complementary therapists, may believe stress is the cause of many human disorders and illnesses, the limitation and danger of this concept as Hawkins points out, is that it doesn't accurately address the source of the stress. It looks to blame external circumstances, without realizing that all stress is internally generated by one's attitudes. It must be emphasized again that it isn't life's events but one's reaction to them that activates the symptoms of stress.

Applied Kinesiology and Reflexology

Reflexologist and massage therapist Kristi Gabriel has an excellent book, *Tapping In For Life: Healing Yourself One Question at a Time*, that may help you in your own growth as well as assisting you with your clients. The book contains examples of how to perform muscle testing and questions to ask on a variety of subjects to find your truth and to assist client's in finding their truth. For more in-depth information on applied kinesiology, refer to *Reflexology: Art Science & History*.

We may now say:

True Power = Life = Spirit;

Force = Weakness = Death

The Issue of the Placebo Effect

Typically speaking, a placebo is anything that seems to be a "real" medical treatment—but isn't. It could be a pill, a shot, or some other type of "fake" treatment. What all placebos have in common is that they do not contain any active substance meant to affect health.

Yet, even though they don't act on the disease, placebos affect how some people feel and can improve their physical condition. According to the American Cancer Society, this happens in one of three people (33%). However, studies indicate estimates of the placebo effect rate range from a low of 15 percent to a high of 72 percent. Placebos have been shown to affect a variety of health conditions, producing measurable, physiological and neurological changes.

The placebo effect has been measured in thousands of medical experiments. Drug companies, for example, must show that their new drugs work better than a placebo (usually this means better than 30%) before the drugs are approved. The placebo effect differs from individual to individual; its strength of effect varies from one disease to the next as does the length of its effect. Part of the power of the placebo lies in the expectations of the individual taking it. It is reasoned, people are used to taking medication and feeling better; thus, if they think they are receiving a drug, the placebo elicits a positive response.

Robert Buckman, clinical oncologist and professor of medicine, says that: "Placebos are extraordinary drugs. They seem to have some effect on almost every symptom known to mankind and work in at least a third of patients and sometimes in up to 60 percent. They have no serious side effects and cannot be given in an overdose. In short, they hold the prize for the most adaptable, effective, safe and cheap drugs in the world's pharmacopeia."

Reflexology and the Placebo Effect

It is interesting that the energy healing of reflexology often works beyond the placebo effect even if the client is not truly open mentally or emotionally to the belief the cellular intelligence of our body has the ability to heal physical, mental, and or emotional issues. The nurturing beliefs of our mind will allow the energy to heal mental or emotional issues. The client's higher self actually directs the energy to where it is needed and can most be accepted at any moment.

Believing or disbelieving in reflexology by the client will not alter the life force. Reflexology operates according to universal principles of life force and electromagnetic attraction, not by our opinions. Reflexology reinforces the concept that more than the brain of those who practice reflexology, or those who receive it, is involved. Life force does not differentiate between physical and emotional pain. Both are simply expressions of blocked life force. The energy flows all by itself according to instructions from the mind. It is, however, helpful as a practitioner to center yourself. This means to gather your attention and be aware of what you are doing. In the nomenclature of today, it means "to be present."

In reflexology studies, when using the single-blind control—this means applying techniques to reflex areas that are not part of the body system being examined—the placebo effect has been noted. The placebo effect may partially explain why for a length of time a client may feel "well" after a session only to relapse. Some clients only need to experience reflexology once, and others must come often to achieve results. Since, in my world, reflexology works to balance the physical, mental, emotional and spiritual subtle bodies that make up the human being, I believe the placebo effect can influence all those realms delivered through stimulation of chemical and neural pathways. I also believe physiological changes do occur beyond the placebo effect involving these bodies, so there are other energetic pathways involved as well in how or why reflexology is effective.

Chapter 7: THE HISTORY OF ENERGY AND REFLEXOLOGY

The saying "There's nothing new under the sun" applies to energy and reflexology. Energy has a long history within reflexology. As noted in *Reflexology: Art, Science and History*, Johann August Unzer (1747), a German physiologist, was the first to use the word 'reflex' with reference to motor reactions in his work published in 1771. This was followed in 1833 with the introduction of the concept and the term "reflex action" by Marshall Hall (1790-1857), an English physiologist. Hall demonstrated the difference between unconscious reflexes and conscious acts in a study on the reflex function of the medulla oblongata and the spinal cord.

Research indicates that the scientific basis of reflexology has its roots in early neurological studies. In 1878 Dr. T. Lauter Brunton published an article in the *Brain, A Journal of Neurology* titled: 'Reflex Action as a Cause and Means of Cure.' In 1893 Sir Henry Head wrote a paper titled 'On Disturbances of Sensation with Especial Reference to the Pain of Visceral Disease.' After years of clinical research, Head established Head's zones (today they are called dermatomes). Head charted areas of skin sensitiveness associated with diseases of the internal organs and conclusively proved the relationship that exists between neurological pathways of the skin and internal organs.

In Germany in 1902, Dr. Alfons Cornelius in his manuscript, *Pressure Points, Their Origin and Significance* (This work was later revised in 1909 and 1933), charted out different classifications of pain according to intensity and the amount of pressure applied to the skin to stimulate the healing process. He found pressure points in the back of the head, then on the feet, and in the inter-rib spaces required the longest time to treat to the point of total lack of sensitivity.

Cornelius discovered localized areas of sensitivity responded to pressure, but the application of pressure also incited other changes to occur in the body. He observed pressure to certain spots triggered muscle contraction, changes in blood pressure, variation in warmth and moisture in the body *as well as directly the 'psychic processes' or mental state of the patient* [this author's emphasis]. He also stated the points he mentioned were long since known to medicine. He even likened the results achieved by the laws of acoustics saying, "One tone can call forth another tone with the similar number of oscillations." Today this phenomenon is called entrainment or resonance. However, Cornelius maintained the consequences of pressure were a purely mechanical hindering of the sensitive neurons of the sympathetic nervous system. I wonder what he would say today with our knowledge of quantum physics and subtle energy bodies.

In Russia, Pavlov was busy with his conditioned reflex—the simple and direct relationship between a stimulus and a response—research which would, in 1904, earn him the Nobel Prize. The writings of Dr. Vladimir Bekhterev (1857-1927), a contemporary of Pavlov, may also be understood to imply that his concept of reflexology involved the subtle energies of the body. He states: "[Reflexology] embraces a special sphere of knowledge to which human thought has not yet become accustomed, and consists in investigating, from the strictly objective standpoint, not only the more elementary, but also all the higher functions of the human being, which in everyday language are called the manifestations of feeling, knowing, and willing, or, speaking generally, the phenomena of psychic activity—the 'spiritual sphere.'"

Dr. William FitzGerald (1872-1942) lists the "soothing influence of animal magnetism" as his first of four reasons for the beneficial effect of zone therapy. It is not known whether FitzGerald listed his reasons in order of importance or not, but the concept of animal magnetism put forth by Dr. Franz Mesmer (1734-1815) is one he most certainly was exposed to in Europe as well as in the United States. The fact that he mentions animal magnetism indicates he believed in the possibility of healing occurring on a mental level. Therefore, can one safely assume FitzGerald felt zone therapy worked beyond the physical body and into other areas?

Dr. Joe Shelby Riley (1856-1947), Eunice Ingham's teacher and mentor, was a well-educated man with many interests and practices including color and light therapy as well as zone therapy. He certainly believed and practiced many vibrational medicine therapies in the era before the Flexner Report.

As evidenced in their writings, Dr. Riley and Eunice Ingham certainly believed in the power of positive thinking and its contribution to the healing process. Positive thinking on both the part of the practitioner and client, when based upon honest and reasonable expectations, is creative and stimulates a change in mental attitude, which offers the opportunity for a readjustment to occur. The key is reasonable expectation. If a chronic condition has been allowed to exist for a lengthy period, irreversible physical damage may have been done to tissue. In this case, a reasonable expectation may not be total healing but a restoration of mobility, improvement in function, and the absence of pain due to the relaxation of stress in the tissue.

All of this was 100 years ago!

One last important historical, scientific reference is to Sir Charles Sherrington. Sherrington established the concept that the essential function of the nervous system was the coordination of activities of the various parts of the organism. His research explained the process by which the brain, spinal cord and numerous reflex pathways control the activities of the body. Through this reflex action, the entire body adjusts to a stimulus or the environment. In 1932, Sherrington and his partner, Edgar Adrian, won the Nobel Prize for their work on the physiology of the nervous system. Adrian also discovered that the electrical intensity of the nerve impulse depended on the size of the nerve rather than upon the strength of the stimulus.

However, light touch in the case of reflexology does not refer to energetic work, for one needs to go deep enough to reach the reflexes to be effective. That said, it always amazes me that reflexology works no matter the depth of pressure applied. I believe this is why reflexologists get results whether they use light or heavy pressure.

The important point to remember is we have to keep asking questions and, in so doing, expand our theoretical knowledge and understanding. All her life Eunice Ingham was highly intuitive and studied the latest developments in health and questioned what she discovered in her physical work and what her intuition revealed to her. Can we do any less? With her progressive mind, it is doubtful she would want us to keep reflexology frozen in the past or restricted to only her ideas as she herself was always pushing the frontier of her mind to take in new concepts of how the body functions and possibly how reflexology works. Eunice often remarked, "Circulation is life; stagnation is death." Was this her short-cut explanation of believing illness and disease are caused by a disturbance in the circulation of life energy and healing occurs when the energy flows freely again?

Chapter 8: EXPANDING OUR REFLEXOLOGY HORIZONS

At the 7th ICR Conference in Hawaii in 1999, Jill Williamson of the United Kingdom introduced Precision Reflexology that reinforces the holistic nature of our work. It relates to the body energetically. Explains Jill, "Precision Reflexology does not focus on a symptom—that is simply the way in which a person describes how they are not well, how their body is out of balance. The manner of their illness often represents the nature of the problem which often mirrors their emotions." Precision Reflexology utilizes a gentle touch, and the concept of "linking," that is, holding two and sometimes three specific reflex points at the same time during a session. Linking is the intuitive art of stimulating the reflexes to be connected and feeling the energy between them. The energy may be felt as warmth or pulse. According to Williamson, "Linking provides access to the subtle body energies of each client, giving an added dimension to each session. Precision work can be seen as a way of combining an Eastern approach to health with a Western one. It is possible to work with the chakra energy of yoga and the physical counterpart—the endocrine system."

Poles of Energy

Working with electrically charged energy flows, Dr. Randolph Stone believes that the body has negative and positive poles, and by stimulating reflex points, in terms of these poles, blockages can be released and balance restored. Stone's polarity therapy recognizes reflex points all over the body.

Polarity therapy indicates that when working with the electromagnetic principles of the body, the left side of the body can be considered to have a negative charge, while the right side has a positive charge. These charges have actually been measured using sensitive voltmeters. The left side of the body is the uptake side and the right side of the body releases stagnant energy. This may be an indication why some reflexologists as they work find the right foot more sensitive due to the release of stagnant energy.

In contrast to Stone, according to Hanna Kroeger, the designation of positive and negative energies applies only to the front of the body. The backside is more complex. For example, the energy in both the right and left leg and heels are negative. The back of the head has a strong positive biomagnetic field as does the base of the spine, but between these positive poles, the spine is negatively charged.

Energy and Reflexology

Dr. Martine Faure-Alderson, D.O. states, "The cranio-sacral system is a "core" system where the control mechanisms of body, mind, emotion and spirit all come together." The cranio-sacral system forms a waterproof bag around the brain and spinal cord. Inside this membrane, the Cerebro-Spinal Fluid (CSF) rhythmically moves as long as we are alive. According to osteopathy and her concepts involving reflexology, to travel in the body, energies use the fluid vessels—blood ducts, Liquid Cephalo-Rachidian (LCR) through the skull, the spine, the fascia, and fluid extra cellular. The energies captured in the external environment are received, transported and stored, allowing the continuity of life. As the result of these constant transformations of energies, obstructions of the fluid vessels hinder the circulation of energies. Reflexology on the cranio-sacral reflexes will stimulate the cerebro-spinal fluid (CSF), bringing about balance of the biochemical and bioelectrical tissue. A release of these strain patterns supports the body in its attempt to return to an ideal state of function and healing."

Energy Healing Practices

Integrative medicine, or what was once called complementary medicine, consists of a range of therapies that fall beyond the scope of mainstream, conventional medicine but may be used alongside it in the treatment of disease and ill health. Alternative medicine, on the other hand, is used in place of conventional, allopathic medicine.

Energy medicine itself is the philosophy, science and art that views the body, mind and spirit as a complex, interrelated whole. Energy healing practices work directly with the natural intelligence of the human energy field to effect healing and create vibrant health. All holistic approaches are based on techniques to influence the energy field that surrounds, courses through, and conditions the human body. Reflexology is only one of many practices that do this. Reflexology can be integrated or used by itself. The goal of the practitioner is to assist the clients on their journey of identifying and removing the blocks (i.e., sensitivity on certain areas found in the feet, hands or outer ears), that prevent them from experiencing and expressing the highest level of health.

Energy practices work directly with the natural intelligence of the human energy field to effect change, create a relaxation response and create health. Healing energy techniques can be divided into two categories: whether or not there is physical contact or non-contact by the practitioner.

Flow of Energy

The natural flow of the universe is from energy to matter; that is, from the energy of the finer subtle bodies to the more dense physical body. Contact therapies include, but are not limited to, reflexology, shiatsu, acupressure, acupuncture, massage, aromatherapy, herbs, homeopathy and flower essences. Some non-contact therapies are qi gong, tai chi, reiki, guided imagery, hypnotherapy, meditation, and biofeedback.

These are all practices involving moving stagnant energy of the physical and subtle energy bodies. Energy healing can assist with a wide variety of physical, mental and emotional ailments. It works with the body's natural capacity for self-healing. It works especially well in overcoming trauma, pain, anxiety and phobias. Each individual's experience of energy healing will be different. So it is paramount to explore a variety of disciplines to find the ones that work best for us either as a practitioner and, therefore, for our clients, and for us personally in our own healing work.

Among all complementary systems is the connection between the spirit and the body, illness and healing. The common thread is that each system involves working on subtle energy levels.

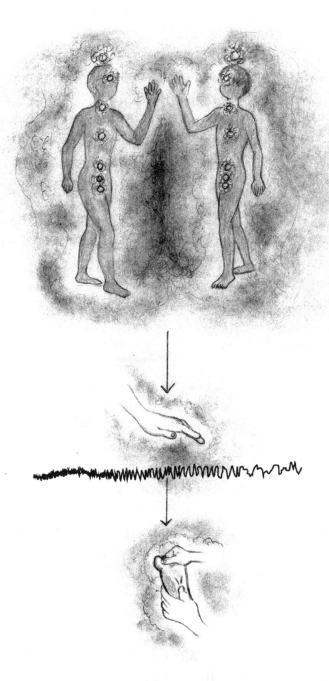

The flow of energy from reflexologist to client

Reflexology, as we know it today, has been linked or combined with complementary energy systems since at least the mid 1980s and the advent of complementary medicine. Books have been written, presentation at conferences made, and workshops conducted, on the combination of reflexology with color, sound, Ayurveda medicine and its chakras, the meridians and five elements of traditional Chinese medicine, Bach flower remedies, aromatherapy, homeopathic remedies, Metamorphic (prenatal) techniques, foot reading, and animal reflexology to name some of these energetic associations. Reflexologists may go on in their education to study other methods of energy work and elect to combine them with reflexology. However, it is essential one studies any system in depth by taking an in-class course before combining it with reflexology.

Disturbances of Energy

The power of energy healing often comes from the early identification of disruptions and disturbances at the level of energy *before* they can manifest in diseases and disorders at the level of matter. This gives us advance notice of problems and precious time to heal our issues before they can create serious illness. For only by healing our issues can we bring our life into balance and achieve vibrant health.

I believe, as expressed above, that all illness begins on the hidden energetic level and if not attended to moves to the denser physical body where it manifests as a pathology. And that since reflexology assists in the movement of the energies in the body, it is possible to reverse an illness before it physically manifests through the application of reflexology. Haven't you ever picked up congestion on some part of the foot, questioned the client, only to have her or him deny knowledge of a problem in the reflected area, and then have the sensitivity go away? Of course, scientifically, the problem here is proving that a pathology was in the process of manifesting and was reversed.

I had a client, an 82-year-old male, whose health was good. However, every time I worked on the lateral aspect on the shaft of the 1st metatarsal of his left foot, just below the head, he would tell me it was too painful and to stop working there. I asked him if he was experiencing any stomach problems, to which he replied no. This went on for weeks. I encouraged him to see his doctor, but he didn't. Finally he went in for his annual physical. Much to his surprise, an ulcer was discovered! Now the ulcer was situated low in the stomach, so it never caused him pain. Apparently, pain is caused if the ulcer is above the stomach fluids, and the lining begins to dry out. So, the client was totally unaware he had a problem, yet I was finding congestion, in the way of sensitivity, in his foot. His negative responses to my inquiries made me question myself and reflexology. The lesson here was for me to trust my findings and intuition. This goes along with an old osteopathic rule to treat what you find, not what you expect to find.

The scientific ability to detect a potential health problem before it manifests may already be available. Technology to measure the electromagnetic disturbances in the meridian system exists.

Electrically unbalanced acupoints, as diagnosed by this technology, has the potential to detect pathology before it occurs. Can't we apply the same research methodology to reflexology?

Healing

No matter how well intended and needed, surgery and prescription drugs result in trauma to the energy field. The history of this trauma must heal itself slowly and sometimes painfully through all subtle energy bodies so that the physical body can truly heal. This is one reason why it takes so long to recover from invasive surgery or prescription drugs, because the energies of the body have become traumatized or poisoned even if the surgery was considered successful by the surgeon.

The body usually records the history of this trauma until it is released. This effect may be responsible for the continued experience of pain after the incision has "healed." Have you ever noticed when an elite professional athlete is injured, he may heal more quickly than a normal person and come back to play sooner? But later, after he retires, he is in constant pain, because he has not truly healed on the energetic levels, and the trauma from the injury suffered years before has not been released.

When healing takes place, it is due to many factors. The application of techniques and the intent of both the reflexologist and the client contribute to the healing process. The restoration of health usually results where there occurs the following conditions:

1. A balance between the body and its inner and outer environments—the body-emotion-mind-spirit connection;

2. A balance between the body and personal relationships—whether at work, school, home, or play with someone else or oneself. Making peace of mind and spirit the primary goal is important;

3. Time—recognizing the body has its own speed of healing, not only externally but internally, that often can't be forced even with drug or surgery; and

4. Relaxation—rest, a change of environment, or a change in mental attitude, which will often create a healing environment and bring about better health.

Chapter 9: CONNECTIONS IN REFLEXOLOGY

The Art of Reflexology

The art of reflexology has many facets, including the healing process itself, which is somewhat of a mystery. The dynamics of the client-practitioner relationship is one component. The connections we have with our clients through touch and who we are as a person is an important connection and explains why we are drawn to do the work we do. Reflexology changes lives; it doesn't matter whether you are the practitioner or the client, the student or the teacher.

Taking in this greater process of the subtle energetic expression of the multidimensional human being, reflexology moves the energies of the body; creates the *potential* for change; and has the ability to detect potential problems before they manifest. I believe that we open our clients to their potential—the potential to change, to change their thought process and, in so doing, to deal effectively with the challenges they face in life and thereby heal—whatever that means to them—and the degree to which they want to heal, consciously or unconsciously.

Innumerable options are open to everyone all the time. Respect for the personal space and boundaries of clients involves giving them the freedom of choice. In the healing process, freedom of choice leaves clients with the decision of the timing and level of healing that is appropriate for them. Accepting this is often a difficult lesson for some practitioners—don't we want everyone to be healthy? Yet, we may be only there as a step along the way in the client's personal journey. It is the quest the clients take to understand their self and their growth process that is important. We are only part of the search, not the end.

No matter how positive we are being, this is a valid reason reflexologists should not have their determination set on forcing the client to get better, or to heal in a certain way or manner, or to a certain level, or in a certain timeframe. To do so interferes with the client's freedom of conscious, or unconscious, choice. Ultimately, clients are responsible for their own state of health. Therefore, the best intention is that the highest good for all concerned occur.

The Dynamics of Healing

The World Health Organization defines health as a state of complete physical, mental, or social well-being and not merely the absence of disease or infirmity. Many people enjoy a state of well-being even though they might be classified as unhealthy by others. As Janet Quinn explains, "Diseases may be cured, but people require healing, and those whose diseases may never be cured may still experience profound healing."

As reflexologists, we are generally in the health and wellness business, not in the sick field that addresses disease and pathology. Wellness cannot just be added to the body in the form of an injection or a pill. It comes from within. Healing is the unification and alignment of the physical body, emotions, mind and spirit. It has little to do with curing of symptoms and ailments. It is a process rather than an event and involves the growth and development of each individual.

Wellness is a course of action—we can't really say we are healthy and expect to remain in that state. Good health is not a state of status quo. It is an endless balancing act—like riding a bicycle where our bodies subtly move to maintain balance. Although some may, I do not know any reflexologist who believes reflexology only works on the physical level. Reflexology has the ability to work beyond the physical into the other parts that make up a human being. Therefore, our role goes beyond simply being a technician to one of being a lay educator and counselor.

The connection between mind and body is immediate, so the body's responses shift and change from instant to instant in response to one's train of thoughts and the associated emotions. Challenges on any level come not to punish us, but to awaken us. Pain is the body's way of waking us up to the need for change; its cumulative effect finally forces us in a new direction.

The Importance of Relaxation

Tension is who you think you should be. Relaxation is who you are.

—Chinese Proverb

In essence, stress is primarily the product of our believing that we need to control our time, our space, or the lives of others. Instead, we have only to give up control and be guided by what is sparked from within. The body is a physical expression of its subtle energy levels, and the real work of our lives is done at those levels. Reflexology, through tactile stimulation, bypasses left-brain rationality to appeal directly to our subconscious right-brain sense that allows healing on the physical level.

Here in the United States, to stay within the law, reflexologists can only work for relaxation. To me, relaxation is the most important aspect of the work we do. Though this may be a "hard sell" to clients who want us to fix their symptom or disease, there is a lot to be said about the importance of the relaxation response identified in the work of Dr. Herbert Benson.

Relaxation of the mind eases tension and creates space for healing to occur. Reflexologists are not the healer—the mind of the client is. We are only the facilitator for the body-mind connection and are creating the opportunity through relaxation for the client's own powers of healing to become activated through time. Though it would be too simplistic to say that the mind causes or cures all illness, it is clear that emotions, attitudes, and beliefs can influence our health and that altering those thoughts and emotions can have a powerful effect on health. Research has shown that healthy people are healthy because of what is going on in their minds, not so much what is going on in their bodies. Regardless of their physical condition, they have the capacity to live life and accept illness as a teacher, not as a punishment but as an opportunity to make lifestyle changes.

Have you had a client get off the table and report feeling wonderful and the chronic pain is gone, and then have them complain the pain returned in a short time? I believe one of the benefits of reflexology is "opening the door" for the client to safely experience what life could be like without their disease, even if it is only for a short period of time. To me, this is the potential of change in operation. Through the relaxation process of reflexology a window is open and the client is given a glimpse of how they could feel or life could be if whatever is bothering them is released, but it is up to them to take action to release the stress and move forward. This, we know, may not be an easy process.

When we move our bodies, we begin creating new patterns. We break the strands that hold us in old habits and postures. Continued reflexology sessions over a period of time are the key if the client is to return to balance. After all, the client didn't develop the chronic condition overnight, so it is unrealistic for them to expect to heal overnight.

One Aspect of Relaxation in My Practice

Many of the relaxation techniques applied by reflexologists are simply natural movements of the foot. Whether or not they infringe on other fields of practice is debatable. In truth, there is nothing new under the sun. How can anyone have a monopoly on the human body and or touch? We may intuitively utilize one or two techniques that apply to the leg from another therapy; however, it is not our intent to practice that therapy without proper training. It is our intent to use techniques that will relax the tissue in the foot and increase our effectiveness in working on the reflexes and bring relief to our clients.

Relaxation of the leg and foot before we begin applying reflexology techniques makes it easier to apply reflexology to softened tissue and makes the client more comfortable. Relaxation techniques can be applied to all portions of the foot and leg all throughout the session, not just at the beginning or the end.

One of the reasons clients seek reflexology is to find relief from the pain of plantar fasciitis. The plantar fascia is a ligament-like band running from the heel to the ball of the foot. This band pulls on the calcaneus, raising the arch of the foot as it pushes off the ground. Plantar fasciitis is the inflammation of the plantar fascia. Oftentimes, the client will complain the foot hurts first thing in the morning with the first steps taken. The pain usually lessens as the musculature of the foot warms up during the day. The primary cause of the problem is in the leg.

Anatomically, the leg is located from the patella down to the ankle—above the knee is considered the thigh. If the foot is bio-mechanically unsound due to tightness of the muscles in the leg, it will be more difficult to obtain optimal results with reflexology. Often, a painful site on the foot will completely disappear once isometric stretches have been performed. This tends to confirm that the pain in the foot is related to the foot itself and not to the reflexes. For more information on isometric stretches, refer to *Reflexognosy: A Shift in Paradigm*.

We can work on the foot and some comfort will occur, but if we want to see a cessation of pain, the leg must be relaxed. It is actually the belly of the *flexor digitorum longus* that tightens and no longer elongates or flexes normally, causing stress on the insertion point in the foot. The belly of the muscle in the leg must be released to increase circulation. Once circulation is increased through relaxation of the soft tissue, reduction of the inflammation and pain occurs and healing can take place. This is just one example of the importance of working to relax the tissue in the leg to help the body heal itself, rather than simply addressing the symptom as it shows up in the foot.

It is up to each of us to pick and choose among those techniques we've seen, experienced, learned and practiced to decide which are the best for our use, resulting in the maximum effectiveness working with our clients.

Is working slowly more advantageous than working fast?

Is it more beneficial to use light to moderate pressure than heavy pressure so that the client can more easily and quickly reach a relaxation response? All reflexologists have their own innate speed of working, just as they have their own unique touch and amount of pressure they use. This may explain why some reflexologists find slower movements and moderate to light pressure, rather than working quickly with heavy or firm pressure, contributes to a stronger therapy that gives them access to the inner depths of the client both physically and emotionally.

The Influence of the Practitioner

We are reminded that health is not just the absence of disease but also incorporates our quality of life. So we may ask: What does the health and wellness model request of the practitioner?

While we must not ignore the fact that we are tools, reflexology, to me, is not an intellectual activity but a sensory one. Reflexology has the ability to work beyond the physical into the other parts that make up a human being. Charts and techniques are cold and sterile. I find it less important to memorize a reflex chart than it is to work both feet entirely, finding sensitive areas and working on them as my hands direct me. The application of techniques that effectively reach the reflexes and the intent of both the reflexologist and the client all contribute to the healing process.

The influence from the reflexologist's hands can be stated in clearly physiological terms. Physiologically, touch to the skin influences the autonomic nervous system. Changes in circulation alter skin temperature. The rates of chemical reactions are proportional to ambient temperature, so a warm or a cool hand near another person can increase or decrease the rates of temperature-sensitive reactions within their bodies. These changes were validated by the reflexology studies performed by Dr. Marc Piquemal of Paraguay.

In addition, we need to consider the effect the electromagnetic output from our fingers, thumbs, and hands have on the energy systems of the client. As a hands-on therapist, we touch not only the skin but contact a continuous, interconnected web-work that extends throughout the body (fascia) and beyond (electrical field). The energy fields projected from the hands of some complementary practitioners are in the range of intensity and frequency that can influence regulatory processes with the body of another person.

Research has shown that fields emitted by practitioners are not steady in frequency but "sweep" or "scan" through the range of frequencies that medical researchers are finding effective in facilitating repair of various soft and hard tissue. It appears that the low frequencies emitted from the hands of some therapists (in the range of 2-20 Hz) are capable of producing beneficial biological effects.

As mentioned above, Dr. Jesus Manzanares' research has also recorded the effect of reflexology on brain waves and found them to be in this range.

Practitioner's Hand Energy Output
Therapeutic Touch Session

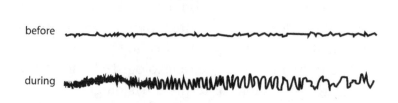

Biomagnetic recording by Dr. John Zimmerman of Colorado School of Medicine, Boulder. Line above is before a session and demonstrates the change in energy output of a practitioner's hand during a therapeutic touch session.

The Importance of Touch

In essence, all forms of therapeutic touch involve far more than simple pressure on the skin as the energy fields of both client and practitioner change from moment to moment in relation to events taking place.

Reflexologists often think techniques are the answer to their effectiveness. "If I learn a new technique, I will be more successful and generate more business," they say to themselves. This has not been my experience, and over my 40+years as a practitioner, I have studied with most everyone, and many techniques are similar—usually it is the philosophy and theory behind the techniques that are different. Techniques will not necessarily make us a better practitioner—it is the quality of our touch that is the most important element in reflexology.

Tools and mechanical devices lessen the element of human touch and support the impersonal nature of technology that is already rampant in our society. The lack of touch is partly the reason that society has become dissatisfied with traditional medicine. Let those of us who are practicing reflexology avoid this same trap of using tools or machines. Reflexology, as a wellness discipline, provides clients the opportunity to find holistic health through the compensating factor of human touch.

Touch As a Mediating Factor

Through the multi-level reaction to touch, in addition to the relaxation response, the client has an opportunity to experience a sense of security, trust, and well-being from which new coping skills may develop. Clients may learn new ways of approaching their worldview simply by being touched.

A challenge often faced is how to help with release of tension at the mental-emotional level as well as the physical. Through the dialogue between practitioner and client, a fresh point of view can emerge and may bring hope and relief from anxiety and stress. This, in turn, can bring on the change in behavior or thinking necessary for healing. To establish this relationship, the client must participate in discussions, which include exchanges of ideas, answering questions, rather than simply receiving instructions or information from the practitioner. When the client becomes active in the process by assuming her share of responsibility toward her health, a positive attitude can be attained and sustained.

The concept of healing touch as a mediating factor is borne out in the work of Stephen Adler, Ph.D., and reflexologist Eduardo Rivera of New York City. In their small study of abuse patients, touch through reflexology allowed all of the subjects to move through their emotional blocks. Having been in therapy for some time, the patients understood intellectually what their psychological blocks were. They were unable to move through the block to begin the healing process until the body, mind, emotions, and soul could be relaxed through reflexology. Touch through reflexology was the mediating factor.

Touch is a component of our physical work. It is curative when we touch someone with healing and compassion in mind. Techniques will not necessarily make us a better practitioner—it is the quality of touch that is the most important element. With the application of touch and pressure to the feet, hands, and outer ears, messages are sent to the brain by way of the nervous system and connective tissue and elicit physical responses from the body, producing, amongst them, a relaxation process. Touch can also bring about an emotional relaxation and release of stress on that level.

Emotional Release

According to Dr. O. Carl Simonton of the Simonton Cancer Center, the most health-supporting emotional state seems not to be enthusiasm or even optimism, but serenity and peacefulness. The ability to be flexible to life's changes can positively affect our health.

Assisting the client in shifting her mental attitude to view changes as challenges or opportunities for growth—rather than obstacles—can come up at any time in a reflexology session and bring on an emotional release and tears. It may not happen often, and we may not think consciously about emotional release in our clients, but our work can open this channel. Reflexology can provoke an unexpected emotional release, and we should be prepared to deal with this by compassionately active listening or respecting the client's privacy if she chooses not to share with us the emotional memory that brought on the release.

The potential of emotional release deserves to be included in our awareness and our reflexology training. According to Lawrence Brammer in his book, *The Helping Relationship*, writes, "While there is a need for specialists trained to cope with the complexities of human problems, most human needs can be met by non-specialist helpers." These people he identifies as parents, teachers, counselors, advisers, mentors, or friends. This is, as Brammer states, "a group of people helping other people to grow toward their personal goals and to strengthen their capacities for coping with life." To this group, we can add the reflexologist.

Brammer contends that often we can apply helping principles in an intuitive fashion. That doesn't mean the reflexologist must be all-knowing and psychic. Providing extra time and attention if an emotional release is brought to the surface during a reflexology session is helpful. Sometimes the quiet reassurance resulting from the feeling that someone cares, or something is being done to help, or someone is willing to listen may be enough. Simple, caring gestures like a hug or saying, "It's okay to feel the way you do," communicates openness to feelings in a nonjudgmental way. However, if the emotions are perceived to be deep or complex, a referral to a psychotherapist is warranted.

Death and Dying

Before leaving the subject of reflexology's impact on the emotional level, one aspect often overlooked is reflexology's contribution to the dying and grieving processes. As a reflexologist works with a terminally ill patient, it is possible to bring calm to the client as she crosses the threshold. The dying individual has the opportunity to share things that may be bothering her that cannot be expressed to the family.

Of significance is an early study conducted by nurses in Switzerland. It found using reflexology on terminally ill cancer patients did not stop the cancer or death, but it did make the patients more comfortable. Reflexology improved the quality of life and led to a more dignified death. Writes Barbara Zeller Dobbs, of the Geneva School of Nursing: "Our purpose for using reflexology with these patients [those terminally ill with various kinds of cancers] was to decrease their pain, but we soon realized the beneficial effect of reflexology on the morale of patients and families. Patients expressed feeling less abandoned, and the families expressed satisfaction at seeing something painless existed that could aid their relative."

On the physical level, research by Gwen Wyatt, R.N., Ph.D. and her team at Michigan State University, conducted on women with stage 4 breast cancer undergoing chemotherapy found the subject's ability to perform tasks in their daily lives improved and most important no side effects of reflexology used as the intervening tool were reported. In a second study with caregivers much the same results were recorded as Dobbs's earlier study had reported.

Extended Benefits

For the survivors, reflexology offers many benefits too. It helps them cope with their loss and acknowledge what was happening. Religious and spiritual values or beliefs may also be questioned at this time. Usually accompanying loss is a search for the meaning of life and death in a broader perspective as a person faces his or her own mortality. Through the use of reflexology, clients may move through the grieving process with more ease. The pain will change over time, but one does not "get over" the pain as if it were some disease that can be healed but rather accepts it as a process—a journey. Those who incorporate reflexology in their grieving process find renewed physical strength to continue their journey.

Remembering that energy can only be transformed; this is the core energy that follows us after death. In "death" or transition, various expressions of the physical body are altered—ultimately culminating in the transition of matter back into light.

Connections with Clients

Working on a client on a one-on-one basis for 30-60 minutes, we find we are connecting with our clients on several levels— the physical, through touching and the release of endorphins; the emotions, through personal attention; the mental, through our thoughts; and the spiritual, through caring and compassion. Reflexology is powerful!

Taking in this greater process, reflexology moves the energies of the body; creates the potential for change; and has the ability to detect potential problems before they manifest. We open to our client's potential—the potential to change, to change their thought process and, in so doing, to heal (whatever that means to them and the degree to which they want to heal). A change in thought process produces a chemical change in the body that can be the beginning of the healing process.

Our responsibility and role in the health of our client must always be taken with the utmost seriousness. Seriousness does not mean with a lack of humor but rather a deep respect and reverence for the other person and humility within ourselves. We have already discussed establishing a bond with our client based on a caring connection.

Our Responsibility

The relationship between the reflexologist and the client has a special and important impact on the healing process. When the practitioner possesses compassion and is dedicated to his client's welfare, the avenue for healing is open. Through the dynamics of this relationship, a new field of activity is created, and within that space, subtle forces work that facilitate the healing process.

Our relationship with the client begins before we physically touch the person. When we initially meet a new client, it is important to take a client history in order to establish a conversation with him or her. In addition, taking the history to discover any contraindication is an opportunity for getting to know something about the individual, and this is the first step in making a connection and building rapport. Although spending time with the client in conversation is not physical touch, we are touching the person psychologically.

Our clients have within themselves the ability to self-heal. While we may encourage clients to take responsibility for their health, as practitioners we have certain responsibilities.

There are ten things that contribute to the effectiveness of our reflexology sessions. The best qualifications a reflexologist can bring with them are our:

1. Own unique talents and who we are as a person;
2. Ability to perform reflexology techniques skillfully;
3. Good theoretical knowledge of all the elements encompassed within the practice of reflexology—its art, science and history—through our education and continuing education;
4. Knowledge of anatomy and physiology;
5. Intentions;
6. Understanding of the interaction of the physical body with the subtle energy bodies;
7. "Tools" —namely that our hands and body—are taken care of properly;
8. Respect and a positive inner attitude toward our clients;
9. Personal and professional integrity by being our authentic self and being honest with clients; and
10. Attention to our own personal growth and development as it reflects in the quality of our touch.

Anatomy and Physiology

Most of the qualities are self-explanatory or have already been touched upon. However, if we aren't supposed to diagnosis why is studying anatomy and physiology in depth important? Is it really more important than knowing areas on a chart?

As we meet clients and take a health history, they will often tell us of their specific complaints. When we are acknowledgeable about anatomy and physiology we are able to understand what body system is under stress and what areas to emphasize on the feet. In turn, when we understand the organs involved in a body system and how the body was originally designed to function we can encourage the cellular memory of the client through not only our hands-on work but by our intention of seeing a particular organ or body system healthy and functioning optimally.

While the concept of affecting the circulation of energy in the body, intention and knowledge of anatomy and physiology are factors in the healing process they are still only part of the story. We can contribute our part by being knowledgeable in anatomy and physiology to the point of coupling it with the intention to affect circulation and the cellular memory of the client's body encouraging it to function optimally.

Ethical Responsibility

During a session, a client undergoes an altered state of awareness or brain waves. In this relaxed state, our client is very open to suggestion. This puts an ethical responsibility on us to be careful in what we say. The right use of positive thought directly affects our clients and encourages them to hope for and expect improvement. Judgmental, rude, or snide comments may plant or re-enforce negative thoughts and actions in the mind of the client. Sharing with the client any medical indication observed or intuited—which may or may not actually be accurate—should be avoided. We do not want to plant worry in the mind of the client. Instead, a suggested referral to a healthcare practitioner is warranted.

Suggestion can be very effective, yet its form is not always the same. Sometimes the quiet reassurance resulting from the feeling that something is being done to help may be enough to calm the client's fears and bring on the breakthrough to health. At other times, it may be our confidence in our ability to help that may open the healing channel. This confidence comes not from our ego but from our heart and compassion.

When we are together with our client, we have created a "community" of two. Community is part of our healing network, all the way down to the level of our cells. A single cell left alone in a petri dish will not survive. In fact, they will actually program themselves to die if they are isolated.

What we see in the single cell is reflected in the larger organism: just as our cells need to stay connected to stay alive, so do we need regular contact with family, friends, and community. Personal relationships nourish us and our souls. Of course, the quality of our communication and relationship with others also influences our cells either in a positive or negative way; the impact is not often neutral. And the road goes both ways. As we nourish our clients by our work and presence, they nourish us.

Closing the Energy Connection After a Session

There are several ways the reflexologist can close a session and break the energy connection with the client. You need to not only release the client's energy but also your part of the connection to them. On rare occasions, you may feel the client's symptoms in your own body. Do not be afraid. They will pass through you. The suggestions below should not be performed out of fear. They are simply a way of clearing your energy, your space, and breaking the connection with the client.

1. Relax your mind and remember to trust the process. Know the life force is connected with the client's innate intelligence and have faith it will do what is needed;

2. After closing, shake your hands and rinse them in cold water to break the connection;

3. Drink a full glass of water;

4. Cleanse the chakras in your hands with your thoughts and visualize Reiki symbols in your palms after you have cleansed them;

5. Smudge the session room with sage. (You can also create a tradition to sage your clients before or after working on them.);

6. In the session room, have a clear or rose quartz or amethyst crystal to collect dead energy. Clean the crystals periodically by putting them in a bowl with ¼ teaspoon sea salt to a pint of spring water and leave overnight;

7. Wear a crystal yourself, making sure with applied kinesiology that it is the correct vibration for you—not too weak or not too strong;

8. At the end of the day, cleanse your aura by taking a 20-minute bath in which you have added one pound

of sea salt and one pound of baking soda, or add one pound of Epsom salt instead, then rest afterwards; and

9. Stay healthy by watching your diet, staying hydrated, getting exercise, meditating or having prayer time, and be sure to take time for yourself.

Why Some People Don't Heal

Unfortunately, as much as we may wish, healing will not happen in all cases. One of the difficulties with conventional medicine and most CAM therapies is that they only look at the physical symptoms and disease. They do not take into consideration the spiritual sphere and its influence on illness; that is, the karma or destiny of the individual as a contributing factor. In this case, illness can be understood as a task to be learned, or something to be worked through. It is sent to balance karma.

In this regard, we can ask: Not knowing this information, what contribution or responsibility lies with the reflexologist? We may feel we know little, can do little, and often feel helpless and inadequate. This is a time when our own personal development is important, and our intention of goodwill and compassion for the client comes into play. Even if we were to know everything, this knowledge must not make us so arrogant that it stunts us by letting our ego hold sway.

It is easy for us, when a client does not come back, to view this as a failure on our part, especially when we sense more reflexology sessions would be helpful. Rather than take this in a negative way, we can change our thinking to the old saying, "No news is good news" and believe reflexology was successful and the client didn't need to come back. Or reflexology was simply not for them. Or that they reached the level of healing they aspire to, or their healing is in the journey—it didn't begin nor does end it with us.

Self-education is a key. We must participate in a conscious path of spiritual development. It doesn't matter the outer form so much as long as the inner growth makes one into a better person: a person who is flexible; has a sense of humor, respect and reverence for all living things; is responsible; and is honest with herself and others. These traits allow us to develop moderation or balance in all things; tolerance; and proper communication with others while preserving our freedom and theirs, while at the same time being open to learning from them.

This, of course, is a life-long task, but through the process comes attitudes of nonjudgment and unconditional love, and the ability to accept whatever level of healing is in the best interest of the client, all without our feelings attached to the outcome. This keeps us in balance between our thinking, our willing—or our application of reflexology and other actions—and our feeling of compassion coming from the right perspective and that our ego is kept out of the client-practitioner relationship.

It is not only a good client-practitioner relationship that brings about change in health status but some change of thinking on the client's part, which enables her to make a successful, conscious or unconscious readjustment to her environment. Restored health may be due to a changed mental attitude or the discarding of—or outgrowth of— an emotional or physical need. Each of these will bring a slight change in the personality. Even if this does not work outwardly in her physical environment or relationships, little by little she may still find new freedom within herself, and it is possible she will no longer need an illness or unhappiness as a way of nudging her forward in her growth. With a sense of knowing that options exist, greater freedom or greater control of thoughts or feelings can occur. Circumstances may not alter, the situation may be as difficult as it was before, but if the client has found a new way of viewing herself and her situation, then perhaps the symptoms of illness need no longer persist. That being the case, she may outgrow the need to see the reflexologist too!

Given the right conditions of time, circumstances, and thoughts, the healing which occurs following a reflexology session may be swift and complete or not at all. While the reflexologist has certain responsibilities, she is not the healer. Healing will only take place when the client's need for the illness has passed and has become at peace with herself, her environment; accepts responsibility for her own health; and develops the courage to change, even if all this is on a subconscious level. The primary aim of reflexology is to relax the body so that it is receptive to healing.

The above has not been stated as an excuse for the *perceived* failure of reflexology, or on the reflexologist's part, or to put undue blame on the client. Reflexologists must accept they are not gods, nor all-knowing. They are not privy to all the dynamics in the lives of their clients, their destiny, nor their lessons in life. Not everyone's destiny is to be well. Illness, as a teacher, is there for them, and if they could learn the lesson some other way, it would manifest in a different form. Their issues and level of health are their business; otherwise, our ego is working when we determine what is best for the client. It is a well-intended ego, but nevertheless it is still ego.

There are multiple factors that contribute to illness, and the primary aim of reflexology is to create an atmosphere so the body is receptive to healing. However, reflexology is not a cure-all for everyone or every condition. For some, the creative process of music, dance or art works better, bringing them joy, deep tranquility and relaxation necessary for the sense of well-being and healing. If our clients do not experience improvement after three sessions, it is time to refer them to someone else or recommend a creative outlet. For them the life lesson may be in the journey, not the application of reflexology.

As reflexologist Barbara Mosier states, "Touching our clients is a sacred act. It may involve a powerful and healing intervention of past traumas when used with clear intention and focused attention; it can deepen self-awareness, self-acceptance, and personal growth, both within the session and in the client's daily life."

Reflexology is the vehicle our clients use to give us permission to share energetic space with them—and this sharing is meant on the deepest of levels. The highest form of respect is for someone to allow us to touch them. We must honor that. On the professional level, the connection between the practitioner and the client has a special and important impact on the healing process. This connection is one aspect that creates a space for healing.

Chapter 10: CONCLUSION

Why Does This Discussion of Energy Really Matter?

In our day-to-day living, we tend to think that science has things pretty well figured out. We forget that the most basic forces in our lives are as yet unexplainable mysteries, although we see the results of energy. For example, we don't know the fundamental scientific basis of magnetism, gravity, or electricity, nor do we need to know in order to make effective use of them.

Although many skeptics still say energy systems of the body as outlined don't exist, we can counter their arguments by saying, until we had the technology to be able to see viruses, they too were only hypothetical. It took the development of the powerful electron microscope to prove their existence. In general, they have been proven through valid, scientific experiments, though many still refuse to believe.

Thinking back over 200 years when Benjamin Franklin flew his kite, tapping into the force of lightning though lightning had always been around the public and scientific community, the population at the time wondered what possible use there was for Franklin's discovery of electricity.

The physical body cannot heal by itself. Yes, it can affect tissue repair, but it does not necessarily heal pain, which is invisible, or let go of the trauma of the injury, which can have an emotional base. The emotional body may heal, and we may feel hope, or experience the release of anger, fear, or sadness and other negative sentiments, but again, this alone is not enough to heal the body. The mind is powerful, but it singerly cannot heal the body. Only when all of our four bodies are in alignment, may healing occur.

I believe healing fundamentally begins with a change of thought process, a change in attitude. Studies have found that cancer survivors positively changed their lives with the diagnosis of cancer and, in so doing, changed their energy field.

There is a growing body of reflexology knowledge, thanks to the research of Dr. Marc Piquemal, Dr. Jesus Manzanares and studies conducted by the China Reflexology Association, that there can be no argument that reflexology does assist in the movement of the energies in the body.

In other fields, such as psychoneuro-immunology and the morphogenetic fields (the study of energy that pervades the planet) and biophotonics, along with more sophisticated advances in bio-medical's recording of the electrical fields, steps are being taken to redefine or add to classical anatomy and physiology.

New Reflexology Hypothesis

As mentioned previously, two of the primary channels for the flow of electrical energy through the body are the nervous and the circulatory systems.

Therefore one could hypothesize that practicing reflexology through pressure on the skin may affect the biomagnetic energy of the body via the endocrine system with the release of chemicals (hormones), the circulatory and nervous systems, through the fascia and the rest of the bodily tissue, and the electromagnetic energy fields spreading out in front of and behind the body.

Going back to Dr. Cornelius' work in 1902, he observed that localized areas of sensitivity not only responded to pressure, but the application of pressure also incited other changes to occur in the body. He found pressure to certain spots on the body triggered muscle contraction, changes in blood pressure, variation in warmth and moisture in the body as well as directly affecting the "psychic processes" or mental state of the patient.

New Definition of Reflexology

Taking into consideration the concept of subtle energy, we may want to think about expanding our definition of reflexology to something like: Reflexology is a practice within integrative medicine which works through the energies of the nervous, electrical, chemical and magnetic systems of the body. With the application of pressure predominantly to the feet, hands and outer ears, it assists the entire body to seek to function optimally.

In Conclusion

As reflexologists, we touch people on many levels—physically, emotionally, mentally and spiritually. The best results with reflexology are obtained when the practitioner's thinking and hands-on work come from knowledge of human nature— both what we know intuitively or have learned, coupled with compassion—and not so much through a knowledge of disease, although a good understanding of anatomy and physiology and the subtle energies of the body are necessary in giving us confidence and our clients faith in our ability.

How we work as practitioners out of our own being using our intuitive nature, and in response to the needs of our clients are our tools, but it is also the connection and rapport we have with our clients, the art of reflexology, that creates the space for healing.

There is absolutely no question in my mind that reflexology works. Our clients tell us that every day. Reflexology is the most holistic, dynamic, and powerful complementary healing practice I know of, and I contend it works on all levels, those seen and unseen.

Reflexology changes lives—it doesn't matter whether you are the client or the practitioner, healthy or dealing with chronic disease, young or old.

And it is our privilege to be part of the reflexology field.

As we began this book, the emerging model of energetic medicine is based on modern scientific insights into the energetic nature of the atom and molecules, as well as the life-energy systems that make up our bodies. These systems connect us to the unified field of consciousness of which we are all a part.

Hopefully, the blending of traditional anatomy, conventional science and biophotonics with subtle energy and the proof of its existence gives rise to energy as the new frontier in reflexology. This may be the next step in the evolutionary journey of reflexology as energetic or quantum reflexology provides new tools for healing and personal transformation.

REFERENCES

This book took over three years to write but 70+ years to prepare to write! The references listed are *only* those actively used in this work.

1. Adler, Stephen and Eduardo Rivera. ICR Newsletter August 1997, 'Use of Reflexology and Hypnotherapy with Sexually or Physically Abused Patients', Litteton, Colorado.
2. Anees Sheikh, ed. Deepak Chopra (1984) *Imagination and Healing.*
3. Beasley, Victor. (1979) *Your Electro-Vibratory Body,* University of the Trees Press, Boulder Creek, California.
4. Becker, Robert and G. Selden. (1998) *The Body Electric,* William Morris, New York.
5. Benson, Herbert & Miriam Klipper. (1975) *The Relaxation Response.*
6. Brammer, Lawrence. (1988) *The Helping Relationship,* Allyn and Bacon, Needham, Massachusetts.
7. Brennan, Barbara. (1987) *Hands of Light: A Guide to Healing Through the Human Energy Field,* Penguin Random House (based on her observation of 5,000 clients and students).
8. Brennan, Barbara. (1993) *Light Emerging: The Journey of Personal Healing,* Penguin Random House.
9. Bruyere, Rosalyn L. (1994) *Wheels of Light,* Touchstone.
10. Cross, John, *Healing with the Chakra Energy System: Acupressure, Bodywork, and Reflexology for Total Health* (2006).
11. Dobbs, Barbara Zeller. "Alternative Health Approaches," *Nursing Mirror,* Feb. 27, 1985.
12. Fare, Elspeth. "Uncovering the Missing Links", *Reflexology World,* March 2015.
13. Forrester, Michael. Source: www.preventdisease.com.
14. Gabriel, Kristi. (2009) *Tapping In: Healing Yourself One Question at a Time,* Denver, Colorado.
15. Gerber, Richard. (1988) *Vibrational Medicine,* Bear & Company, Santa Fe, New Mexico.

16. Gordon, Richard. (1989) *Your Healing Hands: The Polarity Experience*, Wingbow Press, Berkeley, California.

17. Grinberg, Avi. (1993) *Foot Analysis: The Foot Path to Self-Discovery*, Samuel Weiser, York Beach, Maine.

18. Hawkins, David. (1995) *Power vs. Force,* Hay House, Balboa, California.

19. ICR 3rd International Conference Report, Melbourne, Australia, 15-17 October 1993.

20. ICR, 7th International Conference Report, Honolulu, Hawaii, 24-26 September 1999.

21. ICR, 8th International Conference Report, Rome, 21-23 September 2001.

22. ICR, 10th International Conference Report, Amsterdam, 16-18 September 2005.

23. ICR 12th International Conference Report, Anaheim, California, 10-13 September 2009.

24. Issel, Christine. (2014) *Reflexology: Art, Science & History.* New Frontier Publishing, Colfax CA.

25. Issel, Christine and Sandi Rogers. (2000) *Reflexognosy: A Shift in Paradigm,* New Frontier Publishing, Colfax, California.

26. Karagulla, Shafica and Dora van Gelder Kunz. (1989) *The Chakras and the Human Energy Fields*, The Theosophical Publishing House, Wheaton, Illinois.

27. Kircher, Nora. (2006) *Gemstone Reflexology,* Healing Arts Press, Rochester, Vermont.

28. Ko, Tan. (2011) *Traditional Chinese Medicine Simplified,* Infinity Publishing, West Conshohocken, Pennsylvania.

29. Kroeger, Hanna. (1984) *God Helps Those That Help Themselves*, Boulder, Colorado.

30. Lad, Vasant. (1999) *The Complete Book of Ayurvedic Home Remedies,* Three Rivers Press, Minneapolis, Minnesota.

31. Marquardt, Hanne. (2010) *Physical and Emotional Scars, Background Information and Treatment Options*, Konigsfeld-Burgberg, Germany.

32. Myss, Caroline. (1996) *Anatomy of the Spirit*, Three Rivers

Press, New York, New York.

33. Naisbitt, John. (1984) *Megatrends.*

34. Orthlies, Samantha. (2011) *Opening the Senses of the Soul,* Senses of the Soul Publishing, Canada.

35. Oschman, James L. (2003) *Energy Medicine: The Scientific Basis,* Churchill Livingstone, Philadelphia Pennsylvania.

36. Page, Christine. (2004) *The Mirror of Existence: Stepping into Wholeness,* UK

37. Reflexology Association of America, Conference Report, Chicago, April 27-29, 2018.

38. Rosenblatt, Steven and Keith Kirts. (2016) *The Birth of Acupuncture in America,* Balboa Press, Bloomington Indiana.

39. St. John, Robert. (1980) *Metamorphosis: A Text Book On Prenatal Therapy,* England.

40. Seeman, Bernard. (1967) *The Story of Electricity and Magnetism,* Harvey House Publishers, New York.

41. Siegel, Bernie. (1984) *Love, Medicine & Miracles: Lessons Learned About Self-healing From a Surgeon's Experience with Exceptional Patients.*

42. Somogyi, Imre. (1997) *Reading Toes: Your Feet as Reflections of Your Personality,* C.W. Daniels Company Limited, Saffron Walden, Essex, England.

43. Stone, Richard. (1978) *Your Healing Hands The Polarity Experience,* Wingbow Press, Berkeley, California.

44. Egan, Elizabeth, editor. (1997) *Tabor's Cyclopedic Medical Dictionary, 18th Edition,* F.A. Davis Company, Philadelphia, Pennsylvania.

45. Wills, Pauline. (1998) *Reflexology & Color Therapy: A Practical Introduction,* Element, Boston, Massachusetts.

46. Wyatt G., Sikorski A., Rahbar MH, Victorson D., You M., Yang, J., Health-related Quality-of-Life Outcomes: A Reflexology Trial with Patients with Advanced-stage Breast Cancer, Oncol. New Forum, 2012 Nov., 39(6) 568-77 dol: 10.1188/12 ONF 568-77.

CPSIA information can be obtained
at www.ICGtesting.com
Printed in the USA
FSHW011005030620
70642FS